Cochise: Great Apache Chief

The daring exploits of one of America's greatest Indian chiefs. A peaceful leader, he watched the covered wagons swarming through the hereditary hunting grounds of the Apaches, and realized that the traditional roving life of the Indians was ending. The first break in peaceful relations came when Cochise was falsely accused by soldiers of kidnapping, and some of his relatives were hanged. Overnight he was transformed into a bitter foe, but when the Apaches bowed to the white man's superiority, he accepted peace because of his original belief in the brotherhood of man.

Cochise
Great Apache Chief

by
ENID JOHNSON

Illustrations by Lorence F. Bjorklund

JULIAN MESSNER, INC.   NEW YORK

Published by Julian Messner, Inc.
8 West 40th Street, New York 18

*Published Simultaneously in Canada
By The Copp Clark Company, Ltd.*

Copyright 1953 by Enid Johnson
Printed in the United States of America

Library of Congress Catalog Card No. 53-10505

Fourth Printing, 1962

This book is dedicated to Dr. A. Louise Brush
with the deep love and gratitude
of the author

Books by Enid Johnson

BILL WILLIAMS: MOUNTAIN MAN

COCHISE: GREAT APACHE CHIEF

COWGIRL KATE

GREAT WHITE EAGLE
The Story of Dr. John McLoughlin

NANCY RUNS THE BOOKMOBILE

THE RIGHT JOB FOR JUDITH

SALLY'S REAL ESTATE VENTURE
(with Margaret Johnson)

SECOND CHANCE

Contents

Chapter

Foreword

Far back in the Dragoon Mountains in southeastern Arizona, deep among rocky cliffs and canyons, is the Stronghold of Cochise, great chief of the Apaches. In the annals of the Southwest this Stronghold has ever been surrounded with mystery and fame. This was the home of the most warlike Indians in Arizona history, the Chiricahua Apaches. And here their chief reigned supreme.

For centuries the Apache proved himself more skillful and daring in warfare, more cunning in his ability to deceive and elude his enemies, more ferocious in attacking and possessed of more endurance and fortitude under privations than any other tribe on the American continent.

The word Apache means enemy—a name given them long ago by the Maricopa and Pima Indians. They did not call themselves Chiricahua. This was the name of the range of mountains where those of Cochise's tribe lived. They called all Apaches the People of the Woods and themselves Hi-uh-ah which means Men of the Rising Sun.

Military men have said that Apache warriors were the greatest fighting men who ever lived, of any race, in any period of history. And truly during the years of the Indian wars, the Apaches gave the Americans a run for their money! And no wonder! For the American soldier must have a gun and ammunition with which to fight—the Apache a bow and a quiver of arrows. The soldier must wear a heavy uniform—the Apache only a loincloth. The soldier must carry provisions to last months —the Apache could feed himself well on a desert where white men starved to death. The soldier must carry water—the Apache knew every stream and water hole in his whole vast domain. The soldier must take along a change of horses—the Apache rode his horse to death, ate it, then stole another from the Mexicans, the Pueblo Indians or the soldiers themselves.

It was only the inexhaustible supply of white men who could be pitted against them that finally forced the Apaches to give up the uneven battle.

Greatest of all Apache chieftains was Cochise of the Chiricahuas. Frederick Hughes, writing in the Arizona *Citizen* in 1873, said of him: "Cochise was a remarkable Indian. He showed none of the brutish nature attributed to him. It was astonishing to see what power he held over his brutal tribe, for they almost worshipped him, yet no man was ever held in greater fear, his glance being enough to squelch the most obstreperous Chiricahua in his tribe. This was truly remarkable for the Apache is jealous of all restraint and will brook no interference with the exercise of his individual rights."

Savage and barbarous as he may have been, Cochise was one of the great characters of American history. He was mentally and physically superior to most white men who fought against him. In the words of Colonel Reuben F. Bernard, who took over command of Fort Bowie in Apache Pass: "Not only is he the most intelligent hostile Indian on the American continent, but he is one of the greatest military men of all time." Then he went on to say, "All he [Cochise] knows of white men are their evil deeds."

In a rocky fastness of the Dragoon Mountains in an unmarked grave lies the body of this great chief. It is fitting that the surrounding natural fortress is called Cochise Stronghold. It is proper, too, that one of the richest and finest counties in the state of Arizona bears his name.

Cochise was the greatest leader of those who were called: *"La raza bronce que sabe morir"*—"the bronze race that knows how to die!"

First Years

HIGH GRANITE WALLS CARVED BY CENTURIES OF EROSION INTO weird shapes towered around a canyon in the heart of the Dragoon Mountains.

Ghost Face (winter) had departed from the land of the Apaches, making way for Little Eagles, as they called spring. In a small rocky canyon Alope, wife of Nachi, chief of the Chiricahua Apaches, awaited the birth of her child.

Just as Holos, the sun, appeared over the rim of the mountains, an eagle screamed. Then the waiting women—the relatives of Alope, heard a shrill cry, followed by a deathlike silence, and Chief Nachi's son was born.

The baby did not cry again, and so the Apache squaws said

he would grow up to be a strong man—a mighty warrior, maybe. Tze-ge-juni, the medicine woman, picked him up from the ground where his head rested against a piece of wood. Tze-ge-juni considered this an omen.

"Let us call him Cheis," she said to Alope. "On cheis (wood) he lies, and his body is as hard and firm as it is."

The child of Chief Nachi seemed so very strong and vigorous that everyone agreed to give him a name right away, and not wait, as was the Apache custom, until he was at least three months old. Besides, Tze-ge-juni had suggested naming the baby, and her words were listened to with respect.

As Tze-ge-juni sprinkled the sacred hoddentin—the pollen of tule reeds—upon the baby, her wrinkled, ugly face was lit with religious fervor. She muttered prayers and incantations over him as she pointed his little body to the four cardinal points of the compass.

Then Nachi was called to see his son. Taking the baby from the arms of Tze-ge-juni, he, too, moved its body in the direction of the four points, starting with the east where the sun was rising.

The rising sun was a special symbol to the Chiricahuas, for they called themselves Men of the Rising Sun.

As they gathered oak and ash and walnut wood for the frame of the cradleboard, Tze-ge-juni and the other shamans uttered prayers. From the stems of red-barked dogwood, mock orange and Apache plume, they made a canopy to shield his face. Wild mustard was used for the bedding, and a buckskin, painted yellow and decorated with magic symbols, covered the whole.

The baby's head was pillowed on the fur of the beaver, for the Apaches believed that the beaver had power to keep away sickness.

Each of the shamans tied protective amulets on the cradle-board bags of the sacred pollen, turquoise beads and pieces of abalone shell. Tze-ge-juni fastened her own special talisman to it—a piece of lightning-riven wood. And remembering the scream of the eagle at the birth of little Cheis, Nachi attached eagle feathers to it.

Early the next morning the members of the tribe began to arrive for the ceremony of putting Cheis into his cradleboard. The shamans marked the baby's body with pollen and threw more pollen in the four directions. Then the cradleboard was held up four times to the points of the compass, after which the child was placed in the newly constructed cradleboard.

A great feast followed this ritual. The squaws had started the fire by twirling a pointed stick set in a flat piece of wood until it smoked. They blew upon the smoke until a fire blazed brightly. Deer and antelope meat, roasted in the coals, were consumed in large quantities, washed down with tiswin—the weak beer of the Apaches.

As the guests came to gaze at the baby they said prayers for his long life and health, for to the Apaches long life and old age were important goals. Many of them added amulets and pend-ants—such as the paw of a badger, hummingbird claws and pieces of wildcat skin. These were believed to ward off colds and other sickness.

Little Cheis was laced tightly into the cradleboard which was to be his permanent home for several months.

He was such an active baby that when he was only six months old he was allowed to crawl about the camp. His father and the other men of the tribe noted his activity with approval.

As soon as he began to try to walk, the ceremony called "Putting on the Moccasins" was celebrated. Like most Apache ceremonies this was highly symbolic. Cheis was led through four footprints outlined in pollen, the symbol of long life. This was his start at walking the long trail he must follow all of his life.

As Cheis took his first steps, four songs were sung by the medicine man in charge of the ceremony. He sang of Usen, Giver of Life, the great god of the Apaches, who had made the earth and put plants and fruit, deer and antelope upon the land to provide food for the People of the Woods. He sang of the birth of Child of the Water, who was reared under the fire where his mother, White Painted Woman, had hidden him so that the giant who killed human beings would not find and eat him. He sang, too, of the great deeds which Child of the Water had accomplished when he had slain the four monsters—first the giant, next the man-killing eagle, then the terrible buffalo bull and last the antelope which could kill with a glance. And he sang of the time when Killer of Enemies, the elder brother of Child of the Water, had freed the game animals from their underground home where they were imprisoned by Crow, and thereby released them so that they could be hunted for food by the Apaches.

Throughout the ceremony, whenever the names Child of the Water or White Painted Woman were mentioned, all the women present uttered a high-pitched, ululating cry of applause, just as his mother was supposed to have done when the Culture Hero returned home after killing the four monsters.

With the ending of the songs, the ceremony was concluded. Then the feasting began and the gifts were distributed. When the full moon rose over the hills little Cheis was lifted once again to the four directions and prayers were said asking that he grow tall.

By his second spring Cheis was running all about the camp, getting into everything. The tribe was on an expedition to obtain mescal used for food. Mescal usually grows in dry places far away from the camps. Everyone in the encampment, except the very old and the sick, went on those trips. They carried cooking utensils in their burden baskets. As they often stayed for several days, the women built temporary wickiups. While the men hunted, the women gathered the plants and baked them in pits. It was a great time for visiting, for feasting both on the fresh meat provided by the hunters and the vegetables and fruit gathered by the squaws.

In the late afternoons the men and boys ran races, played games and held shooting matches. A great favorite was the hoop and pole game which, like most things in the Apache way of life, was attended with a great deal of ceremonial significance.

None of the women were allowed near the playing ground while the hoop and pole game was in progress, but this did not keep Cheis away. The spring when he was three years old he joined his father to watch the game. It was supposed to make a player lose his luck if anyone stepped on his shadow. But after Cheis had unwittingly run across the shadow of one of the men, that very fellow came off the winner.

"That ish-kay-nay (boy) brings good luck no matter what he does," one of the men commented to Nachi.

And indeed, never did the Chiricahuas have such wonderful luck hunting deer and antelope. The superstitious Indians attributed their good fortune to the presence of little Cheis, who once ran out after his father when he was hunting deer. Nachi wore the usual disguise Apache hunters assumed when going after deer—a mask over his face to which the antlers were attached. His body was covered with a deerskin to enable him to get close to the animals before they knew that a human being was anywhere near.

Nachi crawled toward the unsuspecting animals and then

loosed his arrows. After killing three deer he found that he had no more arrows in his quiver. Cheis had noticed his father's predicament. Holding a bunch of bear grass before his little body, he crawled right up beside his father and handed him two more arrows. So quietly and unobtrusively had he moved that the deer paid no heed to him. With those arrows Nachi killed two more fine fat bucks.

That night around the campfire one after another of the tribesmen sang the praises of the clever little boy. His father beamed proudly and patted his son on the head.

By the time this period of fun and work was over, each of the families had enough food preserved and stored away to last through the months of Ghost Face. Some of the food was stored in their individual wickiups, but most of it was hidden in large caves in secret places—secure from the depredations of the wild animals. The entrances to these caves were sealed with rocks covered with a plaster made of mud.

During the winter months, as they sat around the fires in their wickiups, the men repaired their bows and made new arrows. They scraped the handles of their spears and polished the bone points. Cheis helped with this work at a very early age, by steadily holding the end of the bow while his father tied wet sinews onto it.

As he grew older Cheis loved to listen to the stories the men told as they relaxed around the fires during the long winter evenings. His favorite was the one which was always told while the men and women played the moccasin game. This was the legend of long ago when the world began and the creatures had held a contest for daylight. The birds wanted daylight, but the beasts preferred to have it always dark.

To play the moccasin game the Apaches lined up, facing each other on opposite sides of a fire which had been lit in an open place. They played this game, which was really an elaborate version of the old-fashioned American game of "button, button, who's got the button?" just as the birds and animals were supposed to have done. Sometimes they used moccasins in which to hide the bone counters, but oftener they just had four holes in the ground on either side. Those doing the hiding held a blanket in front of them so that the opposing side could not see in which hole the bone had been hidden.

All during the game the players sang the songs which told about it. When the one whose turn it was to guess had made up his mind in which hole the bone counter had been hidden, he struck it with a stick.

As the game progressed, the players presented in character the songs of the many creatures found in the legend. The songs of the small birds were given in high falsetto voices. The songs of the animals—and the giant who took part on the side of the beasts—were given in harsh, gruff tones. Each player pretended to be either a bird or an animal.

How Cheis loved the part when, according to the legend, the animals had lost all but two counters, and the little wren sang happily, "Daylight is coming! Daylight is coming!"

The birds, of course, eventually won the contest. Then they began killing off all the animals. They tried, particularly, to kill all the "bad animals." However a few of those, such as the bear, the owl and the snake, managed to escape. Those three creatures were always considered very dangerous by the Apaches.

Someday, Cheis told himself, he, too, would be big enough to take part in this game as well as in hunting and raiding with the grown men. How he longed for that time to come!

Chapter 2

Boyhood

WHEN CHEIS WAS LESS THAN A YEAR OLD HIS FATHER, Chief Nachi, had married a second wife, who bore him a son named Juan. Later Nachi took a third wife, who in due course bore him a third son. This boy, called Naretena, though a weak and sickly child, was soon to show himself as possessing qualities rare in an Apache—pity and deep sensitivity. As soon as Naretena had learned to talk and was able to run about the camp, he and Cheis became great friends.

Each of Nachi's three wives had her own wickiup, but they were near enough so that the three squaws shared the work of preserving and cooking food, tanning deerskin and making garments for themselves, their children and their mutual husband.

Upon the death of his mother just a year after he was born, Naretena was taken to live in the wickiup occupied by Cheis and his mother, Nachi's first wife Alope.

Of Nachi's three sons, Cheis was always the favorite among his tribesmen. Everyone predicted that he would be a great hunter, remembering the time when, but three years of age, he had carried arrows to his father with which to kill deer.

When Cheis was six he was given his first bow and arrow, by his father's uncle Nah-kah-yen (Keen Sighted). Nah-kah-yen took over Cheis's training in order to prepare him for the chase, the hunt and the raid, which was the Apache way of life.

It was a great day for Cheis when his great-uncle presented him with such a weapon.

"Before you can become a hunter," Nah-kah-yen said, "you must be a good shot." So, using arrows which had been sharpened—for at first he was not allowed to have flint arrowheads —Cheis spent many hours each day learning to shoot.

He found that it was not always easy to hit the mark, but he persevered until he became expert. He used to challenge his playmates, most of whom were two or three years older than he. Oftener than not, Cheis came off the winner, and gathered up the arrows of the losers as his prize.

As they grew older the boys played many games with bows and arrows that helped them acquire skill. As Cheis got more and more proficient with his small weapons, he longed to be taken on a real hunt with the men of the tribe. But for that, of course, he must wait. Meanwhile there were many other things he could learn to do. His uncle made him a war club and a spear from the yucca-like plant called the sotol. Then Cheis asked for a shield like the one his father used in warfare. With Juan and other boys of the tribe he played a make-believe game of raiding.

The young boys often brought into the camp small animals they had caught. Like true Apaches, they never wasted arrows on turkeys or rabbits. They caught turkeys after running them up and down hill until the birds were too tired to fly. Then the boys killed them by hitting them on their necks with clubs. Rabbits, too, they killed with clubs after chasing and surrounding them.

To cook a rabbit, the squaws buried it, fur and all, in a bed of hot ashes. After it was baked, the skin and insides were removed and the meat cut up and eaten.

The Apaches liked meat with fat on it. They rubbed the fat on their legs as they ate it, too, believing that it would make them fast runners. Nah-kah-yen told them a story of an Apache boy who lived long ago, who always ate all the fat on his meat, being too greedy to use any of it on his legs. One time, when it was necessary to run away from his enemies, his legs rebelled, refusing to carry him. "Run with your belly," his legs told the gluttonous youth.

In order to be strong enough to endure the severe life of raid and warfare that faced him, Cheis and the other boys were taught to harden their muscles. They knew that often on the raids or the warpath they might be obliged to go for days with nothing to eat and drink, and that they would have to travel long distances over rough terrain. To prepare for this, they had to take long runs over rough country with a heavy load on their backs. Every morning, after a brisk run up and down the mountainside, Cheis and his fellows were ordered to plunge into the icy stream.

Nah-kah-yen trained the boys to run with their mouths

closed by giving them each a mouthful of water before they started off on a long cross-country run. Upon their return they were told to spit out the water. Often one or another of the boys had swallowed it. But Cheis always managed to return to the starting point with the water still in his mouth.

Always, after a raid, Cheis listened avidly to the warriors' tales. He knew all about the rigors of the hunt, the hardship and glories of war, the cruelties of the enemy. Like all Apaches he was taught from his earliest days to be suspicious and distrustful of all other peoples, whom they regarded as enemies.

Young Cheis devised for himself tests of character to show his bravery. Once he put some dry sage on the under part of his arm and set fire to it, allowing it to burn to ash. Nor did he flinch from the pain of the burn, though he carried the scar it made for the rest of his life.

Often Nah-kah-yen matched Cheis against other boys, telling them to wrestle until one of them whipped the other. No holds were barred. They also fought with slingshots. By dodging the flying stones, they learned to keep from getting hit. By fighting with bows and arrows they acquired skill both in taking accurate aim and in avoiding getting hurt.

When Cheis was ten years old he began to practice handling and riding horses under all sorts of conditions. He rode bareback, up and down steep hills, controlling his mount with his knees. Galloping at full speed he picked up objects from the ground. He learned to halt his horse just before reaching a barrier, as well as to jump it over high hurdles.

Cheis knew that he must never allow himself to appear "soft." No matter what was asked of him he must willingly comply. Nor must he ever allow fatigue or pain to show on his face.

One of the tests of endurance given the boys was that of

forcing them to stay awake for two whole days and nights, being allowed no food or drink during the entire period.

And now Cheis had reached the stage when his mind as well as his muscles must be trained.

One moonless night Nah-kah-yen took Cheis and four of his companions out to follow a trail, which passed over grasslands and through groves of mesquite. It crossed a wash which had a little water in its bed. After walking all night they had to find their way back to the camp by their own wits. This was to teach them not to get lost.

Cheis received many lessons in stealth as well. He was taught to rise straight up from the grass on which he was resting, in order to surprise an enemy and take him off guard.

"You must not only sit still, you must think still, too," Nah-kah-yen told his pupils. "If you do not wish your enemy to know your plan, you must not even think of it when he is near you—until you are ready to kill him."

Nah-kah-yen often took the boys to the great pasture of grama grass near their camp and ordered them to take cover when he gave the signal. They must make themselves invisible in any way they could. Cheis learned to conceal his brown body in the green grass, having first covered himself with tufts of it so that no one could distinguish him from the surrounding undergrowth. He became so skillful at this art that it often appeared as if the earth had opened up and swallowed him. He learned to hide behind shrubs and gray rocks, too, so that no one passing or even standing near by could see him. He sprinkled himself all over with earth so that he was indistinguishable from the boulder behind which he hid.

Important, too, to the Apaches was their way of signaling and sending messages to their companions in times of war or raid. Fires for these signals were made with leaves, grass and pine or cedar boughs, so that the smoke would be so dense it could be seen for miles. Cheis learned to read these signals as well as make them. A sudden puff rising into a graceful column from a mountaintop, which was then quickly extinguished, indicated the presence of a strange party passing on the plains below. If the puff was repeated and multiplied, it told that the travelers were not only numerous but well armed. Steady smoke maintained for some time meant a call to scattered bands of Apaches to collect at some specified place. If these signals were made at night, when smoke could not be seen, fires were used to convey the same messages.

The boy learned to read other signs besides smoke signals. He was soon able to tell from the condition of the grass over which travelers had gone, just how recently they had passed. He could tell, too, whether they had been Indians or Mexicans by studying their footprints. If they were Indians he even knew to what tribe they belonged, for each tribe wore a distinctive style of moccasin.

The time which had elapsed since the passage of the travelers was accurately computed by studying the discoloration of the herbage or by breaking off a few stalks to determine the amount of natural juice still left in the crushed grass. They knew the size of the party by the number of tracks they had made.

Bent twigs, broken branches and marks on the trunks of trees all carried messages. Stones lying on one side of the trail without any apparent arrangement told the Apache much. For he could see that those stones never "grew" that way, but had been so placed to call attention to the spot toward which they pointed.

"You can tell when a stone has been moved," Nah-kah-yen told the boys, "because it won't have any dirt upon it. If it has been turned all the way over it means that the raid has been unlucky. If it is only partly turned over, it means that the expedition has been a failure. But if the stones are left in their natural places with the heaviest sides down, it means the raid has been a success."

One bright morning the shrill cry "Choddi! Choddi!" (Antelope! Antelope!) was heard in the camp. So the Chiricahua hunters formed a party to go out after this favorite food. Cheis received permission from his father to accompany them. He was twelve years old at this time, and eager to prove to the braves of the tribe that he was ready to take his part with them.

A special shaman who had antelope "power" prepared the heads that were to be used by the hunters in stalking the game.

First he took all the bones out of the heads, leaving the horns and ears. All the time he worked on the masks he accompanied the task with the special ceremonial songs which, so he believed, would give the men who wore them the benefit of his "power."

As they neared the game the hunters scattered, making a big circle. Cheis had covered his bronze body with the skin of an antelope, placing one of the masks upon his head. He crawled close to the herd. Then he began to walk like an antelope, holding a stick in his hand.

By exercising great patience the hunters were able to get within arrow shot of the antelopes before the herd was frightened away. Cheis's arrow hit one of the largest, fattest antelopes killed that day. How proud he was!

He skinned the animal, being careful to obey the rules which Child of the Water had first given the Chiricahuas. He must put the head of the kill toward the east; he must never walk in front of it, nor straddle the animal while butchering it. He carefully removed the sinews to take to Alope, his mother, to use for thread.

In order to insure good luck in the future, Cheis cut out the heart of the first animal he killed and ate it raw. He also left some of the entrails as a gift offering to Crow, saying, as he did so, "This is for you, Crow. Make me lucky and we will have food all the time, you and I."

Although he longed to keep the hide for himself, he must obey the rules of his tribe and give it to someone else. So he carried it back to camp and presented it to his great-uncle Nah-kah-yen.

That night around the campfire the hunters made much of Cheis because of the fine fat antelope he had killed.

Soon now, Cheis hoped, as he listened to their words of praise, the braves would allow him to go on the first of the four raids he must engage in as a novice before he could become a full-fledged warrior. But even before becoming a war novice he must go off by himself for two weeks in the woods and live by his own wits.

Chapter 3

Cheis Gets His "Medicine"

AND SO THE DAYS FILLED WITH HUNTING, WITH LEARNING the lore of the Chiricahuas and taking part in their ceremonies, passed happily for Cheis, until three more years had gone by. Once again it was the season of "Many Leaves." The beautiful trees and native grasses had turned a rich green in the Dragoon Mountains where the Chiricahua braves were resting after an extensive raid into Mexico.

This had been very profitable, for the braves returned with many horses, mules and captives. There was a score of small Mexican children—both boys and girls—and a few frightened women who were parceled out among the squaws to help with their labors. All the adult male Mexicans the Chiricahuas en-countered had been speedily killed.

The boys of the tribe, led by Cheis's brother Juan, took great delight in tormenting the Mexican children. This sport would not be permitted for long by the older Chiricahuas, for it was their plan to make good Apaches of the young Mexicans. They would be trained exactly like their own children, and would eventually marry into the tribe and help build it up. But their first few days in camp were filled with horror.

Cheis found no pleasure in torturing either animals or children, as most of the boys did. Although he took no part in such "sport," himself, he never interfered with the others when they did so.

Not so Naretena. He could not bear to watch the boys forc-ing the little Mexican captives to run barefoot on the sharp spines of cactus, whipping them with switches of cottonwood if they faltered.

"Stop!" cried Naretena, when he saw his half brother Juan tormenting a small Mexican girl and laughing at her cries of pain.

Naretena rushed at the tormentors, brandishing one of his father's war clubs.

At that the boys turned upon him. Throwing him to the ground, they removed his moccasins and gave him a dose of the same treatment they had been giving the captives.

Unlike the Mexican children, Naretena made no outcry. He ran on the cruel cactus spines until he fell down in a faint.

At that moment Cheis came upon the scene, rushing to the defense of his little brother whom he loved better than any-thing in the world.

When they saw the fury in Cheis's eyes the boys ran away.

But Cheis followed and found Juan hiding in the wickiup of his mother.

"Come out, gut of a coyote," Cheis called. Taking Juan by the hair he dragged him from his hiding place, and challenged him to a fight.

Although nearly a year younger than his brother, Juan was large for his age, and was both taller and broader than Cheis. But Cheis's strength matched his and he was far more agile.

Juan grabbed Cheis by the wrist and twisted his arm around his back, exerting pressure upward. Cheis bit his lips in pain. Juan kept up the pressure until it seemed that he must surely break his brother's arm. Cheis managed to catch Juan under the leg with his free arm and threw him, forcing him to release his grip.

In another moment Cheis was upon him, digging his knee into Juan's groin and pinning his arms and shoulders to the ground. Then, wrapping his sturdy legs around his brother's waist he began to squeeze. Juan's face was distorted with pain—his eyes grew bloodshot. At last he cried, "Enough!"

Cheis got up and pulled his brother to his feet.

"Next time I'll kill you," he vowed between clenched teeth, then he walked away, followed by the admiring glances of the other boys who had crept out of their hiding places to watch the fight. There was a look almost of adoration on the face of Naretena, but he said no word of his love and gratitude, for that was not the Apache way.

Naretena knew that never again would Juan or any of the boys of the tribe dare attack him.

For several days after this incident Juan kept away from both of his brothers. This grieved the affectionate and peace-loving Naretena. One day, finding his brother alone, he said, "We eat the same food, walk the same earth, breathe the same air—and the same sun is over us. Let there be peace between us, my brother."

With these words Naretena won Juan, who, as long as he lived, never again tormented him.

At last the time came for Cheis to go alone into the wilderness for his two weeks' testing period. While away, he would "make his medicine," entering the forest where, free from interruption, he would find a quiet spot and stretch upon the ground to receive his dream. In this dream, so the Apaches believed, a bird, a reptile or an animal—which was to be his guardian angel throughout his life—would appear to him.

Cheis had to make elaborate preparations for this journey. First he must be fitted with new moccasins. These his mother made out of a piece of rawhide which she had soaked in muddy water until it was pliable. When the hide was dry Cheis stood upon it, while his uncle traced the outlines of the soles of his feet with a sharp knife. Then Alope sewed leggings of soft doeskin to the soles, using some sinews Cheis had brought her from a deer he had killed. The toes of the moccasins turned up at right angles and ended in a disc about an inch and a half in diameter, to protect his feet from sharp stones and cactus.

The moccasins reached halfway up his thigh, and the tops were pushed down below the knee, making folds in which small articles could be carried. These and a breechclout, also made of deerskin, and a narrow headband completed his costume.

Cheis must make new weapons, too. He found some long pieces of flint and inserted them into the shafts, wrapping them tightly with sinews. These flints, he firmly believed, had once belonged to the Thunder People, some of the many gods of the Apaches.

From the skin of a mountain lion he made a quiver for his arrows. He sharpened the end of a seven-inch stalk of sotol for his spear. He made a new bow, also, curving and bending it back and forth until it became elastic, and used the sinew from the loin of a deer for a bowstring.

He worked for days making his stone knife, chipping it with another stone until it had a point, sharp and deadly.

When all of his new weapons were made, he took them to a shaman to be blessed.

Then he put a fire drill in the quiver with his arrows, and at last Cheis was ready to go. He arose early, blew a little pinch of hoddentin to the sun, as he said, "Be good, O Holos. Make me find my medicine."

He went into the sweat house which had been constructed by a special shaman. He took a sweat bath not only for the sake of his health, but because he believed it would bring him good fortune. When he came out of the sweat house he plunged into the stream.

Before leaving the camp he went into his mother's wickiup and said solemnly, "May we live to see each other again," which was the Apache way of saying good-by.

He gave Naretena a stalk of sotol wood and a small knife. "Make a notch on this stalk every morning," Cheis said. "When there are fourteen notches on it I will come back."

Without a backward look he turned and ran off toward the crags that rose almost straight up from the camp.

Cheis carried neither food nor water with him. For during this testing period he must provide those necessities for himself.

The first afternoon he found a small, well-hidden canyon where water seeped out from between rocks. There he drank his fill. That night he had no food, for the Apaches believed a man must fast in order to have his "medicine" appear to him.

Although it was late spring it was very cold on the mountain heights, and Cheis was almost naked. But an Apache is never bothered by discomfort, nor does he ever complain of either the burning heat of day or the freezing cold of night. Cheis lay down on the hard ground and fell asleep. He dreamed that he was leading a band of warriors on a raid into enemy country. In his dream he and his warriors were about to be attacked by soldiers of the enemy, when an eagle, flying overhead, warned them of their danger.

Cheis awoke with excitement. Now he knew! Itza-chu—the Eagle—was to be his "medicine."

In the morning, immediately after arising, Cheis took a pinch of hoddentin from the small buckskin bag fastened to his waist—without which no Apache ever traveled anywhere. He blew it toward the sun, thanking Holos for having sent him his "medicine."

Now he must make his tzi-daltai—his talisman—and he decided that his should be in the likeness of an eagle.

Near by he saw the blackened stump of a lightning-riven pine. He searched around the trunk until he found a flat piece of wood three inches long and less than an inch wide. He tied this to his G string and started to climb up the nearly perpendicular cliff that rose above him. Slowly, carefully, he crept up and up. A single slip would have hurled him to his death on the sharp rocks below, yet he moved confidently higher and higher, until he reached a spot far above the canyon floor. There he seated himself against the cliff. Taking his stone knife from the fold of his moccasin, he started to carve his tzi-daltai. For more than an hour he worked—until he had made a crude figure of an eagle with outspread wings.

Now that he had had his dream and made his tzi-daltai, he no longer needed to fast. He was very hungry, but there was no game to be found on the heights to which he had climbed. To reduce the pangs of hunger, he tied a deerskin thong tight around his waist. He was thirsty, too, so he put a small stone into his mouth to start the flow of saliva.

He climbed down, down the steep mountain until at last he found himself on a dry and sandy plain dotted with greasewood and sage, with here and there a clump of mesquite beside a dry wash. He knew that the nearest spring was fifty miles away and he had had nothing to drink for many hours, but he did not worry.

As the sun started to set he came to a spot in the wash where the mesquite grew thick upon the bank. Here he dug a hole in the sand in the center of the wash. In a few minutes he felt a little moisture on his fingers. He dug deeper and made a small basin into which a little water slowly filtered.

While the basin was filling he cut a strong branch from a mesquite tree and hunted around until he saw a pile of leaves and earth heaped untidily among the stems of a large bush. With his branch of mesquite he beat upon this pile until several frightened pack rats scurried out of their nest. He killed a couple of them by giving them a blow on their heads with his mesquite club, but as he reached to pick them up he felt a sharp stab on the back of his left hand. He looked down in time to see a large rattlesnake gliding away from the pack rat nest. Quickly he jerked a buckskin thong from his waist and wrapped it tightly around his left wrist. With his thumb and forefinger he caught another rat just as it was scurrying past him. Holding it just back of its neck so that it, too, could not bite him, he cut a deep gash in its side from which the blood spurted. Using the bleeding rat as a poultice, he clapped it on the punctures which the snake's fangs had made on his hand. When the rat had died from the poison in the snake wound, Cheis caught others which he used in the same way. The sixth rat did not die, even though he held it on the snake bite longer than he had held the others, so then he knew that all the poison in the wound had been absorbed. His hand was stiff and sore, but no great harm had been done.

But the anxiety of those minutes had made his mouth dry. Perhaps by this time enough water would have collected in the hole he had dug to quench his thirst.

When he returned to it he found that the hole held almost a cupful of water. Through a hollow reed which grew beside the wash, he gratefully drew the water into his mouth.

Dusk had fallen as he started off toward the purple mountains. Great plains stretched as far as he could see, cut here and there by rugged ravines worn by the ravages of storms and crisscrossed by chains of sharply pointed mountain peaks.

Morning found him still trotting along over the barren plains. After his long night's journey he was hungry and very thirsty. He came to a squat little barrel cactus, knocked off its head and removed the pulp which he squeezed, managing to get a few drops of liquid.

On and on he ran, until by midmorning he reached a low mesa or table-top mountain where he found some acorns. They were not ripe but they made a meal of sorts for the hungry boy.

The days passed. Often he was hungry. Oftener still, thirsty, but he became adept at finding water, and there were enough roots and berries on the land through which he traveled to sustain him.

One evening he smelled wood smoke which apparently was coming from a campfire at the mouth of a canyon. Cheis knew that no Apache would choose such a place for a camp where one must shout to be heard above the sound of the near-by mountain stream.

Cheis went close to the camp, where he saw a huge fire which sent sparks all over the trees and underbrush. What manner of man would build a fire of that size?

Silently he crept closer and looked down upon three strange creatures. Apart from a few Mexicans, the only people Cheis had ever seen were Indians. Could these men be "White Eyes" perhaps? A few members of his tribe had once seen some white men. They were different from Mexicans, the enemies of his people. These men were enemies, too, Cheis told himself, for everyone who was not of his tribe was a potential enemy to the Apache.

Cheis spent the whole night watching them. As they sat cross legged around a blanket, they seemed to be playing a strange game, with small oblong objects like pieces of wood, though not so hard. Cheis did not know it, of course, but the three white men were playing a game of three-handed pinochle. He watched them as with great ceremony they picked up one card at a time. Perhaps this was no game, Cheis thought, but some strange medicine of the white man, for he noted how serious they looked as they picked up their cards and gazed at them long and steadily. He was even more baffled when one of the men swept up a handful of some bright looking chips that sparkled in the firelight, and uttered words in a strange tongue, followed by a loud "haw-haw."

After a while the white men stopped their strange game and began to cook something on their campfire in a round pan with a long handle. This food gave forth a smell that sickened Cheis, and he saw, to his horror, that they were cooking fish—a food which no Apache would touch. In disgust Cheis moved far enough away so that the nauseating odor no longer reached his nostrils.

Later, when it had faded from the air, Cheis returned to his vigil. Now the men were apparently going to sleep, for, two at a time they lay down on blankets, while the third man kept watch, holding something that looked like a long stick in his hands.

Next morning two of the men went off, followed at a distance by the young Apache. Whenever one of the men turned around, Cheis darted behind boulders or bushes. But for all his caution he was examining them closely. Their faces, he noted with repugnance, were covered with hair. No Apache ever allowed hair to grow on his face. Whenever it appeared he plucked it out with crude tweezers made of pieces of flint.

The strangers wore shirts and long pants stuck into heavy boots that made a great deal of noise when they walked on the stones and rocks of the mountain. And each of them carried one of those strange long sticks. These must be some sort of a weapon, Cheis thought.

Then he remembered his father's describing something he called a "pesh-e-gar" (rifle) which he had seen in the hands of Mexicans on his raids into their country. Nachi had said that this was a wonderful thing—that it could shoot twice as far as an arrow could reach. Cheis wished they would use those pesh-e-gars so that he, too, could see how they worked.

Very soon he got his wish, for some distance ahead of them, about two arrow shots away, Cheis saw a black bear coming along the trail. Bears, Cheis knew, were very dangerous animals. Just the smell of them brought on a dreadful disease called "bear sickness." And even if one didn't get sick, he would come under its evil influence if it were near him.

Cheis was about to turn and run, when he saw one of the men lift his pesh-e-gar to his shoulder. There was a report so loud that it nearly deafened the boy—and the bear fell dead in its tracks.

How Cheis longed to own one of those shooting sticks! With such a weapon he would be the greatest hunter in his tribe. And think what he could do to their enemies when he would be taken on one of the raids into Mexico with the braves of his tribe!

Even though he was shocked at their killing the bear—for bears, as well as being dangerous, were also regarded as sacred creatures by the Apaches—Cheis's admiration for their marksman ship knew no bounds.

He watched as the men took long hunting knives from their pockets and skinned the bear, carrying the hide and much of the flesh back to their camp. They built up the fire and put great hunks of the bear meat on the coals. They were going to eat it!

For the next two days Cheis watched the white men as they went about their strange affairs. He was surprised when he saw them scratching away at stones in the bed of the stream with long-handled instruments which had sharp crossbars on the ends. After several minutes of hacking, they stopped and seemed to be looking for something in among the rocks. What were they searching for, Cheis wondered?

The third day the same two men left the camp, while the other one stayed behind again. As Cheis watched, the man began chopping down some trees to replenish the fire which was already much too large by Apache standards. The man had left his rifle leaning against a near-by tree. Cheis eyed it covetously. Could he possibly sneak in and get it without the man's seeing him?

But he dared not run the risk, though he stayed near the camp all that day, watching for a time when the white man would relax his vigilance.

When the sun went down the soaring granite turrets and pinnacles of the mountains glowed crimson against the darkening sky. Cheis watched in vain for the return of the other men, but night fell swiftly and silently and they did not come back.

When Cheis saw the man starting to eat more of the bear meat he moved far away from their camp, for he could not bear to watch such sacrilege.

Perhaps in the morning the white man would go after more game, and he could follow and see how he made the wonderful pesh-e-gar ready to use.

But by this time Cheis himself was hungry once more, for all during his spying on the men he had not eaten so much as a root or a berry.

The day before, while he was following the two men, he had noticed some deer tracks in the sand. Deer meat would taste very good, Cheis thought. So next morning he used a method learned from Nah-kah-yen of luring a doe within shooting range. He blew on a whistle made of a leaf which he held horizontally against his lips, making a sound so much like the cry of a baby deer that soon a fine fat doe appeared. Cheis stopped and fitted an arow to his bow, at the same time placing two more arrows between the second and third fingers of his right hand, ready for use should the first shot fail to reach its mark.

But Cheis did not need to use those additional arrows, so expert a hunter had he become. He killed the doe with the first one.

Then he skinned his kill and cut some pieces of venison from the carcass which he cooked and ate. Not far away he found a cave where he hid the meat he did not immediately eat, covering it with boughs of cedar.

Having satisfied his hunger and safe in the knowledge that he had enough meat cached away to last for the remaining days he must be away, he returned to watch the man. Perhaps now he would be able to see what the man did to the pesh-e-gar to make it shoot.

But when he finally did see the man load the rifle he lost all desire to own it. For what a lot of trouble it involved! First the man poured something that looked like gray hoddentin into the opening at the end of the pesh-e-gar. He covered this with something too small for Cheis to see what it was. Next he put a thing into the hole that looked like a small round stone. After this he stuck a long bright stick into the opening and pressed down upon it. He then removed the stick.

It was some years later before Cheis learned the proper words for what he had seen the man doing. First he had poured powder into the muzzle of his flintlock rifle; then he had put a patch over the powder, a lead bullet on top of that, finally ramming it down into the muzzle of the gun with a ramming rod.

Bows and arrows were much better, Cheis told himself. All one had to do to make ready to shoot them was to fit the arrow into a bowstring. Why, your enemies could easily kill you while you were doing all those foolish things, he thought. And the game, too, after the first kill, would run too far away to be reached, frightened off, as they surely would be by the loud noise of the first shot. Now that he no longer wanted to own the white man's weapon, Cheis lost interest in watching them.

According to the notches he had made on the stick he carried in his quiver, like the one he had given Naretena, Cheis saw that his time in the wilderness would be up in two more days. He had started toward home when he saw the tracks of a large cougar. How fine it would be to have a cougar skin to take back to the camp of his people!

He followed the tracks in search of its lair. They seemed to lead along the bank of a small river. Cheis climbed a large cottonwood tree the better to look around. The branches of the tree reached far out over the stream.

After a moment he was distracted by the scream of an eagle flying directly above him. He looked up. There, on a large branch a few feet away and gazing fiercely at him was a huge cougar. Cheis looked at the beast but made no move. The cougar began lashing its long tail, its powerful claws tearing at the bark of the limb on which it crouched.

Suddenly it sprang, landing on the exact place where Cheis had been. But with great coolness the boy had dropped into the stream just as the cougar made ready to spring. Enraged at being deprived of its prey, the cougar tore great strips of bark from the limb, growling fiercely.

Cheis swam under water until he reached the place on the bank where he had left his bow and arrow before climbing the tree. Carefully taking aim, he brought down the great beast with two well-placed arrows, then watched it fall to the ground. If Cheis needed further proof that the eagle was his "medicine," he had it then. For it was the eagle's scream that had warned him of danger.

What a wonderful trophy he had to take back! He would ask his mother to dress the cougar skin and then he would give it to his beloved brother Naretena, to keep him warm when Ghost Face came again.

But, before he returned he had one more thing to do. He

must snare an eagle which was to be his "medicine" for the rest of his life, kill and stuff it and carry it back with him.

First Cheis killed a rabbit which he placed on an open spot on the sand. Then, with loops of sinew, he made an Indian trap of snares around the rabbit's carcass. The loops were in the form of slipknots tightly drawn. Next he carefully covered the loops with bunches of grass and leaves. Then he lay hidden behind a bush as he waited with true Apache patience for an eagle to appear.

Late that afternoon an eagle stepped into the trap. Out bounded Cheis from his hiding place, caught the bird and clubbed it to death. Cutting it open, he stuffed it with moss and sealed it with clay from the riverbank. Now his "medicine" was intact and he could return home.

That night, as he neared the camp of his tribe, he looked up at the mountains silvered with moonlight and out across the dim, mysterious plains. He heard the old familiar voices of the night and drank deep of the fragrant air, filling his lungs with its perfume.

Tomorrow as Holos showed himself over the rim of the Stronghold, Cheis would be home with his people—his two weeks' testing time successfully accomplished. He had proved he could care for himself when alone in the wilderness. He had found his "medicine" and made his tzi-daltai. He was happy and content.

Chapter 4

War Novice

UPON CHEIS'S RETURN A FEAST WAS GIVEN FOR HIM. AL-though no word of praise was spoken to him either by his father or anyone else in the tribe, he knew he had made good in their eyes.

It was good to be back in camp after his lonely two weeks—good to smell the deer meat stewing in a clay pot on the fire in his mother's wickiup and to know that there was food ready for him whenever he wished to eat.

Now that his testing period was accomplished, Cheis longed more than ever to be taken on a raid into enemy country. Young Apaches must go as "novices" on four raids before they could be admitted into the tribe as warriors. Cheis was fifteen, tall and strong. He knew that his father was planning a raid for horses in five days' time. Did he dare ask to go?

One evening, just as Holos was ready to hide for the night, Cheis went to his father's wickiup. He stood silently before him until Nachi gave him permission to speak.

"Soon I will be a man, my father," Cheis said. "I wish no longer to remain in camp with the old men, the women and the children when the braves go upon the warpath. In five days you go to Mexico to get horses for our people. I wish to go with you."

Nachi eyed his son as he spoke. For some time he did not answer, and Cheis feared that perhaps he had angered him.

At length the chief said quietly, "Nachi has watched you and is pleased with you. It is true that you are young to start on the warpath, but maybe not too young. On this raid Pionsenay is to make his first trip as a war novice. You may, too. Go now to a high place and pray to Usen. Then take your medicine—your tzi-daltai—to Nan-ta-do-tash. He will bless it for you." Nachi paused for a moment and then said, by way of dismissal, "I have spoken."

Cheis wanted to run and shout with joy, but that would not do. Without a change of expression he turned and walked away. That night he climbed alone to the highest spot in the Stronghold to pray to Usen for strength, for skill, for everything a warrior needs but courage. Cheis had no need to pray for that. He had courage aplenty.

All night he stood on the high place, praying to Usen and to the four winds. When the Big Dipper, timepiece of the Apaches, had crossed the sky and faced downward, he knew that morning was near.

He climbed down the almost perpendicular cliff and ran swiftly to the wickiup of Nan-ta-do-tash, the medicine man.

"In four days I go upon the war trail," Cheis said. "All night I have prayed to Usen for strength and wisdom. I bring you my tzi-daltai to make it strong for me."

Part of a job of a medicine man was to discourage young aspirants, so that none but the bravest and strongest would go on the warpath.

"On this raid we go far into Mexico—to the foot of the sky. Those who go must be strong men. It is no journey for weak boys," Nan-ta-do-tash said scornfully.

"I am strong enough," Cheis replied between clenched teeth.

"Danger lurks every foot of the way once we have entered Mexico," the medicine man went on, tauntingly. "We will meet many of the enemies of the Men of the Rising Sun. Those who go must be stronghearted [this was the Apache way of saying brave]. They must not cry out with fear when faced with danger."

"I am brave enough," Cheis answered stoutly.

Nan-ta-do-tash gazed steadily at the youth, but Cheis did not drop his eyes.

At last the shaman said, "Today when Holos stands high in the sky come back to my wickiup. You and the other novice, Pionsenay, must learn the warpath speech before you can leave with the braves. Go now, Dikohe."

Cheis knew what it meant to be called "dikohe." A dikohe must instantly obey every order his elders gave.

When Cheis and Pionsenay returned at noon to the lodge of Nan-ta-do-tash, they found that the shaman had made the first of the different helmets they must wear on each of the four raids. The helmet was a buckskin hat, colored yellow, and decorated with a black zigzag design representing lightning. After sprinkling it lavishly with pollen, he said a prayer over it and placed it on Cheis's head. Then he blessed the other objects he must carry with him. Most important were the scratch stick and the drinking reed. For one strict rule for a war novice was never to scratch his head or his body with his fingers. The scratch stick was made of cedar three inches long and half a finger in thickness. Nor must a novice permit water to touch his lips. He must suck it up through a tiny reed. Both the scratch stick and the drinking reed were attached to a long leather cord and fastened to the belt of his breechclout.

There were many taboos surrounding the young novice. He must act as a servant to the older men and obey their every order. Yet, for all this, a boy accompanying the braves on a raid for the first time was considered by them to be a source of power. During the first four raids he was called "Child of the Water." So in spite of the heavy tasks imposed on him by the braves, he felt his own importance.

The warpath terminology which both Cheis and Pionsenay were obliged to learn seemed utterly meaningless. For example, pollen was not called "hoddentin," but "that which becomes life," because the Apaches believed that it brought growth and vitality. The chief he must call "he who is wise for me," and night became "that which is first visible" and day "that which is well seen." Both Cheis and Pionsenay worked hard to master all the ambiguous phrases.

The fifteen braves and two novices who were to go on this raid into Mexico met before the wickiup of Chief Nachi, who spoke to them in solemn tones. "You love your homes and children," he said. "But we are going to leave them. Forget them. We do not know what is going to happen. Prepare your weapons. Do not be afraid. We want to accomplish something for our camp. Our people are in need of what we are going to bring to them."

What activity there was in the camp! The men refurbished their bows and arrows. They made war clubs, using a round stone the size of a man's fist, covered with rawhide and attached by a short length of hide to a wooden handle. These clubs, about twenty inches long from stone to handle and painted red and black, were very deadly.

They cut ropes, too, from pieces of rawhide, braiding several strands together to make them strong. As well as being used for tying horses, they were flexible enough for lassos.

When all was ready, the braves took their weapons to Nan-ta-do-tash, who sprinkled them with hoddentin and prayed that they would destroy their enemies.

On the night before they were to leave the tribe held a war dance in which both novices participated. The whole tribe assembled in a large cleared place. A great fire was lit and, one by one, the men who were going on tomorrow's raid were called upon to show what they would do to the enemy.

Even though the two novices would not be permitted to do any fighting, they, too, were called upon to perform. When at last the name Cheis was called, the youth darted out into the center of the circle, his face contorted with fury as he leaped into the air, then dropped to the ground dodging from right to left as though avoiding the arrows of the enemy. As he danced, the old men of the tribe watched attentively. They were judging him on both his alertness and agility. That he performed to the satisfaction of all was proved by their shouts of approval.

After the dance Cheis was almost too excited to sleep.

Early in the morning the braves gathered before the wickiup of Chief Nachi. The shamans painted their bodies and faces red and black. They trotted off behind their chief.

Nan-ta-do-tash accompanied the warriors. He would be consulted all along the way—and his advice acted upon. The prayers and ceremonies of a medicine man were considered necessary to insure the success of a raid. Everyone was careful not to break any of the rules, and every command of both Chief Nachi and Nan-ta-do-tash was obeyed instantly.

They trotted for miles over the rough trail. The two boys were glad of the strict training they had undergone. They did not stop for food at midday, but kept on until evening. Nor did any of them take a drink of water from the heavy water bag which Cheis carried.

That night, when Chief Nachi at last called a halt to make camp, Cheis and Pionsenay built the fire and cooked food for the braves. They roasted pieces of deer meat on sticks and served each member of the raiding party.

The novices were not allowed to eat until the food had grown cold. Then they must stand guard while the braves slept. Shortly before dawn they received permission from Chief Nachi to lie down for a short sleep.

Early in the morning Nachi led his braves toward the south. He went far off the well-known trails and never crossed an open space until he or some of his most trusted warriors had scanned it carefully. For the enemies of the People of the Woods were everywhere.

After three days of steady travel they entered Mexico, and now their vigilance increased. The shaman painted the moccasins of the braves with the sign indicating the four corners of the compass in order to prevent them from taking the wrong trail.

Now they were forced to face a long march without water. At the last water hole Cheis had filled his water bottle and coiled it over his shoulder. The sun beat down mercilessly, making the water hot, but Cheis ran lightly along without a word of complaint.

He carefully heeded each move of the experienced warriors and listened to their every word, eager to learn all he could.

High in the mountains of Sonora, Nachi made camp. From this point he could see so far across the great valley that no enemy could get near him undetected.

Two scouts, who had been sent ahead, came back to report that a wagon train was coming up the valley. Soon, in the distance, tiny specks appeared. All day the Chiricahuas watched this Mexican caravan. The scouts who had been close enough to see it plainly, reported that it was composed of twenty-six wagons, each drawn by eight mules and driven by well-armed Mexicans.

"The drivers keep their wagons close together and ride with their weapons always at their sides," said Klosen, one of the scouts. "When they camp they make a circle of their wagons, with the men and mules inside. Two well-armed men are always on guard."

"Sometime they will get careless, maybe," said Nachi. "Cheis," he called, "come here."

Cheis went quickly to stand before his father. "Go down to the Mexicans' camp and watch them. Get as near to them as you can. Come back at dawn and tell me all that you have learned."

The boy had no time to eat. But his excitement at having been chosen for such an important task drove all thought of hunger from his mind. Without a sound he darted down the hill until he came near the camp of the Mexicans. Although it was too dark for the Mexican freighters to see him, nonetheless he never relaxed his wariness.

Using a branch of mesquite as a shield, he crept close to the wagons. All his training in remaining still and disguising himself stood him in good stead.

He could hear the freighters talking. From the many Mexican captives brought to the Chiricahua camp, Cheis learned enough Spanish to understand what they were saying. Some of them were complaining because they must stand guard during the night.

"There isn't an Apache within two hundred miles!" one of them said. But the captain of the caravan vowed he would take no chances on losing the valuable goods they carried, to say nothing of getting themselves killed.

Cheis listened carefully when the men spoke of the place at which they would stop next day for their noonday rest, and where they expected to camp on the following night. He noticed that each of the drivers kept a loaded pesh-e-gar—like the one he had seen at the camp of the white men—beside him when he slept. If the braves of his father's band should attack the caravan at night, the Mexicans would be ready for them.

Shortly before dawn the direction of the wind changed. Cheis noted this as he carefully crawled farther away from the wagon train, still holding the bush between himself and the Mexicans as he watched the mules.

First one of the mules and then some of the others raised their heads and sniffed. Cheis knew that this meant they had caught his scent. If the Mexican guards saw this they might guess the cause.

The guards did notice. They, too, looked anxiously out into the night. From his hiding place behind a bush, Cheis gave the weird cry of a coyote. When they heard this the guards relaxed, for they thought, as Cheis had meant them to, that it was the smell of a coyote that had disturbed the mules.

Just as dawn streaked the sky, Cheis returned to his father's camp and reported all that he had learned.

For the next two days the Chiricahuas followed the Mexican

caravan. During the whole time every move the drivers made was noted by Nachi and his band. Noiseless and invisible, they stalked the slow-moving wagons mile after mile.

Nachi saw that the Mexicans were least on guard during their noonday rests, when the drivers were tired and sleepy. And since they could see in every direction over the vast, and apparently empty plain, they felt safe.

The chief knew every foot of the territory over which the wagon train was going. So he and his braves went on ahead, leaving one of his band behind to trail the Mexicans and give warning if anything unforeseen should happen.

Noon of the third day grew near. Great clouds of dust arose, all but obscuring the wagons from the watchful eyes of the Chiricahua brave who followed in their wake. Soon the lead wagon stopped and the others drew up around it. They had reached the place where they planned to rest.

The sun was like a brass helmet as it beat down mercilessly upon the scorched earth. Not a breath of wind stirred. A deathly silence pervaded the land.

The captain of the wagon train believed that he and his party were the only creatures alive on the whole vast plain. Even so, he ordered one of the men to stand guard. This man looked enviously at his mates who had stretched themselves in the shade under the wagons to doze.

Soon all the men were snoring. At last the guard could stand the burning sun no longer. He, too, crawled under one of the wagons.

Little did he guess that lying completely buried in the sand beside the road, disguised by bushes held in front of their faces, the Apache braves were waiting to attack.

When he saw that the guard as well as all the other Mexicans were fast asleep, Nachi rose. The sand dropped from his painted body, naked except for his moccasins and breechclout. At this sign the braves crept forward, surrounding the wagons. Then from the throat of every warrior issued the frightening Apache war cry.

The guard had scarcely left the shelter of the wagon, when a young Apache brave felled him with his war club.

And now all twenty-six Mexicans of the caravan rushed out from beneath the wagons, armed with their rifles. But they never had a chance to fire them. They were met with the lances and war clubs of the Chiricahuas. The few who were not slain in the first rush tried to run away, but they were immediately killed by the arrows from the bows of the pursuing braves.

And now that they had killed all the Mexicans, the Chiricahuas went among the dead and smashed their skulls with blows from their war clubs. Unlike most Indian tribes on the American continent, Apaches very rarely scalped their victims.

From a safe distance Cheis and Pionsenay watched, longing to take part in the battle. For this they must wait, Cheis thought grimly, until they had completed three more raids as novices. But the boys did have a chance to take an active part, for during the battle many of the mules had broken loose and started to run off. Swinging their rawhide ropes over their heads, the boys took off after them. Lassoing the mules one after another. they led them back and tethered them to the spokes of the wagon wheels.

When the Chiricahuas examined the contents of the wagons they found much of value. First they took the twenty-six rifles which had belonged to the slain Mexicans. Then they gathered together many knives, kettles and blankets which they loaded onto the backs of the captured mules.

Leading the mules away from the wagons, the Chiricahuas

then set the vehicles on fire, after which they set off in the direction of the Sierra Madre Mountains.

After they had gone a full hundred miles, Nachi gave the order to stop and make camp. Cheis and Pionsenay killed and skinned one of the mules and built a fire, and soon the braves were feasting on the best-loved delicacy of the Apache— roast mule meat.

Then the braves sat around the fire, boasting of their exploits, while the mules grazed peacefully in the thick grass of a near-by meadow under the watchful eyes of the two novices.

Although they had gained much loot and many excellent mules, they had not accomplished the purpose of this raid, which was the acquisition of horses. Therefore they counted it a failure.

Nan-ta-do-tash went into a trance, after which he spoke to Nachi of a large ranch in Sonora that they both had seen on previous raids. There a wealthy rancher kept a large herd of splendid horses. They could reach this ranch by making a short detour. They planned to stay near the ranch for a few days to study how best to capture the herd with little loss to themselves. The braves were already tired but Apaches never gave in to fatigue.

To revive them Nan-ta-do-tash brought out his bag of hoddentin and put a pinch of it upon the tongue of each brave, then sprinkled more on their heads, for they all believed that the sacred pollen gave them strength. Cheis and Pionsenay were sent to gather nettles with which the braves lashed their legs until the blood came, for this, too, relieved exhaustion, they thought.

Nachi selected five of his most agile braves to accompany him to the ranch. He ordered the remaining warriors, under Nan-ta-do-tash, to proceed toward home with their heavily laden mules, arranging to meet in five days' time at a certain place beside a stream. How Cheis longed to go with the chosen five to help capture the horses!

The braves under Nachi took only their bows and arrows with them, for they must be unencumbered by heavy weapons. On and on they journeyed until they reached a grove of cottonwood trees near the great ranch where the horses were kept at night. For two days and nights Nachi and his five braves studied the situation. They found that just before dusk every day the herd was rounded up from the meadow where they grazed and were driven by the vaqueros (cowboys) into a corral which had stone walls ten feet high. After putting the horses in the corral, the vaqueros closed and locked the heavy iron gate. Just after daybreak each morning they opened the gate and turned the herd out to graze.

On the third night the Chiricahuas watched while the vaqueros drove the horses into the corral. Then, assured that they were safe from thieving Indians, the vaqueros went to their bunkhouse and ate their evening meal, after which they amused themselves playing cards and strumming their guitars until nearly midnight. One of the braves watched beside a window of the bunkhouse until he saw that all the vaqueros had gone to bed and were asleep. Returning to Nachi, he reported that all was clear.

Then the Chiricahuas scaled the wall and dropped into the corral. So little noise did they make that even the watchdogs, chained outside the bunkhouse, were not disturbed.

All night they moved among the horses, stroking them gently and speaking softly to them. Each of the braves selected the horse he thought strongest and most swift on which to ride on the morrow. Then, with the patience of their race, they waited for daylight.

As the first light showed in the sky, the unsuspecting vaqueros stumbled sleepily out of their bunkhouse and went to the corral. One of them turned a large key in the great iron lock and threw the gates wide open. Immediately Nachi and the five braves mounted their chosen horses. With bloodcurdling yells they stampeded all the other horses, driving them off toward the mountains. The thoroughly duped vaqueros could only stand with open mouths, staring in unbelief. Nor had they any means of following the stolen herd, for every horse on the ranch had been taken by the Indians.

Meanwhile the main body of warriors, under the leadership of Nan-ta-do-tash, made its way to the meeting place. When they got there they waited almost two days for Nachi and the five braves.

Cheis grew very anxious. Had the hated Mexicans captured his father? Had he been killed? He knew they were not lost, for Apaches never lose a trail, even on the darkest night. They had left signs along the way—signs so slight that none but a member of their own tribe would even see them, let alone interpret their meaning.

At last Nachi and his braves came upon the others, beside the stream just over the border in New Mexico. Cheis's fears were changed to joy when he beheld the seventy-five wonderful horses. One especially—a fine black stallion—caught his eye. How he longed to have that horse for his very own. He had already given it a name—Intchi-dijin (the Black Wind).

The braves shouted with glee when they heard how the horses had been captured from right under the noses of the stupid, sleepy vaqueros. Oh, how Cheis wished he could have been there and taken part in that thrilling capture.

By nightfall of the following day they would arrive at their own camp. Nachi sent a messenger ahead to tell his people that the victorious braves were returning with much loot, with none of their number killed and only a few superficial wounds.

As they neared their camp they saw that the Victory Fires were burning, sending their glow on the stark crags surrounding the camp. The voices of their people, raised in song, came to them.

When they arrived they were met by cries of joy. Before the feasting and dancing started, Nachi distributed the loot, giving every member of the tribe a share. Especially did he make presents to the widows whose husbands had been killed in previous raids. As he handed out the twenty-six rifles to his most trusted braves, he told them that, beginning in three days, they must learn how to use them.

Then it was time to distribute the horses. Why did his father delay giving away the black stallion, Cheis wondered. At the very last, when every other horse had been presented to one of the people, his father put his hand on his son's shoulder. Then he handed him the reata which was around the horse's neck. Intchi-dijin was his!

Cheis was too overjoyed at his great good fortune to say a word, but his eyes glowed with love and gratitude and something akin to worship as he met his father's gaze.

Then the feasting began. The squaws had prepared quantities of deer and antelope meat when they learned that the victorious heroes were coming. And they had brewed great quantities of tiswin, the favorite beverage of the Apaches, made from fermented corn.

They feasted until they could hold no more. Then the singing and dancing started. A band of male singers intoned the refrain, beating on their drums made of rawhide stretched over huge pottery bowls, while Nan-ta-do-tash chanted the half-sung, half-spoken prayers.

Then he called upon one after another of the returning braves to come forward and dance. Before the raid the dancers had shown what they were were going to do to their enemies; now they demonstrated what they had done. On such an occasion a man was called by his own name. The use of the personal name acted as an exciting challenge to the brave.

At last the people called:

> "Nachi, they say to you.
> You! You!
> They call you again and again!"

Then the chief of the Men of the Rising Sun stood before his tribesmen and spoke of the brave deeds done by his warriors. To everyone's surprise, he mentioned, though briefly, the names of the two novices, Chels and Pionsenay, saying they had behaved well and would soon become warriors worthy of a place in the band.

And so for four nights and days the feasting and dancing continued. Then, on the morning of the fifth day, the mules were all slaughtered and the squaws jerked the meat. It was stored in one of the secret caves to be used when Ghost Face came again and there could be no hunting.

Chapter 5

Cheis Becomes Cochise

NACHI HAD ORDERED THE BRAVES TO LEARN TO SHOOT WITH the rifles taken from the Mexican wagon train, but not one of them knew how to load them. Even Cheis, who had once seen a rifle loaded, failed to do it correctly, for he had missed seeing the white man cover the powder with the all-important patch.

"We will have to capture a Mexican who has knowledge of these pesh-e-gars," Nachi said. So two braves left camp and returned a short time later with a Mexican they had caught.

Nachi promised him his liberty if he would instruct his braves on the use of rifles, but the thoroughly frightened Mexican did not, of course, believe the word of an Apache. He did manage, however, in spite of his fear, to teach a few of the Chiricahuas how to load the rifles. Then he fastened buckskin targets to nearby trees, and the braves blazed away at them.

Only about half a dozen of the tribe, besides Cheis and Nachi himself, became proficient in their use. Most of the braves did not care for these new weapons. Some said it took too long to make them ready, and everyone agreed that they made too much noise to ever have any value on the hunt. Most refused even to try.

Apaches were an independent people. Although they must obey their chieftains when on the warpath, at camp each man was a law unto himself.

Nachi was furious with the Mexican because he was tactless enough to show his surprise when at last, taking him a hundred miles from camp, he set him free.

"No Man of the Rising Sun ever speaks with a forked tongue [lies]," Nachi told the trembling Mexican. "Go back to your kennel, dog of a Mexican!"

Meanwhile Cheis longed to hear that another raid was being planned. He wanted to complete his novitiate quickly, so that he could be a full-fledged warrior. But there was still a goodly supply of loot left from the last raid, so Nachi was content to remain in camp for a time.

However, in the season called "Earth is Reddish Brown" (late fall) he organized a trading expedition north to the Navaho country. Apache squaws made almost no pottery and they had need of clay pots for cooking. Loading a quantity of freshly tanned skins of the mountain lion—which the Navahos prized highly—on the backs of several burros, fifteen braves started off, mounted on horses stolen from the Sonora rancher.

Cheis went on this expedition in the hope that it might turn into a raid, even though it started out as a peaceful trading mission. As their way to the Navaho country led through territory roamed over by occasional bands of Comanches—deadly enemies of the Apaches—there was good reason to believe that his wish might be fulfilled.

The second day after leaving camp, Nah-tanh, who was scouting well in advance of the main band, backtracked to report that a group of thirty Comanches were driving a flock of sheep stolen from the Navahos toward their home on the plains. At once Nachi changed his plans. Sending three of his braves with the burros to the Navaho country, he led the rest to a point some miles in advance of the place where Nah-tanh had reported seeing the Comanches. His plan was to cut them off. The spot which Nachi had chosen so craftily was a natural trap, made by a deep crevasse about thirty feet wide which lay between two steep banks.

When the Chiricahuas arrived at this place Cheis was put in charge of the horses some distance away. It required all his skill to keep the restive horses near enough to the braves in case they were needed to make a hasty getaway, and far enough from the crevasse so that their movements would not betray their presence to their approaching enemies.

As night fell a bitter wind began to blow. They dared not kindle a fire for fear the Comanches might smell the smoke, although no flames would show, so cautiously did Apaches build fires. Cheis distributed some jerked mule meat and a few handfuls of parched corn to each of the braves. With this scanty food and fresh water from a near-by spring, they would have to be content. But if there had been no food at all, the Chiricahuas would have borne it with their usual stoicism. Often, on a raid, they went several days without eating at all.

Their capacity to stand cold matched their ability to endure hunger. Nonetheless, Cheis looked forward eagerly to the warm suit made from the skin of one of the soon-to-be-captured sheep which would be his.

All night the Chiricahua braves watched at the eastern end of the crevasse for the Comanches to appear. All night Cheis guarded the horses. All night the wind blew on the nearly naked bodies of the braves.

At dawn next morning they heard the hoot of an owl. This was the signal from Nah-tanh, who was stalking the Comanches, announcing that they were close to the trap. Nachi replied with so perfect an imitation of the owl's call that the Indians on both sides shivered, for they believed that owls were the ghosts of the dead.

And now they could see the sheep coming toward the western end of the crevasse. They allowed more than half of them to enter the trap before they attacked. Then, with a fearful yell, they loosed a flight of arrows. The frightened sheep added their bleats to the din as they tried to escape up the steep sides of the crevasse. As this was impossible, those in front attempted to turn back, but were met by the onrush of the sheep behind them.

Meanwhile the arrows of the Chiricahuas had killed two Comanches who were leading the flock. More arrows fell upon the others, who by this time were speeding arrows of their own toward their foes. Several Chiricahuas were struck, but they nonchalantly pulled the arrows from their bodies and went on fighting. Only one, a young brave named Satl, was badly hurt. He fell and was about to be trampled by the hoofs of the panic-stricken sheep, when Nachi called his son to go to Satl's rescue.

As Cheis ran to the assistance of the wounded brave, an arrow struck him in his upper left arm. This was the first wound he had received, and although the pain was great he was elated, for at last he was taking a real part in battle. He tried to pull the arrow out, but it stuck firm. So, paying no more attention to it than he would to a gnat on a summer day, he helped Satl to his feet and dragged him out of the crevasse and onto the level ground above. By this time his arm had become numb.

Meanwhile the battle between the ten Chiricahuas and thirty Comanches waged furiously. After half an hour's fighting, five more Comanches had been killed and as many more wounded. The others, though greatly outnumbering their foe, were no match for them. They abandoned the stolen flock and escaped into the forest.

It was a hard job turning nearly a thousand sheep back the way they had come, but the Chiricahuas accomplished it. Nachi selected several pairs of the strongest sheep and lashed their horns together with thongs of rawhide. He ranged these pairs on either side of the flock, making a sort of animal fence which kept the ones inside from wandering off. On both sides he stationed some of his braves, who kept the sheep moving by frequent pricks of their lances. In the fore of the flock two warriors led the way, while others followed in the rear.

Cheis was ordered by his father to take Satl and the horses back to camp. "If you reach camp safely with all the horses," Nachi said, "this will count as the second raid of your novitiate." He helped his son lift Satl onto the back of one of the horses. Then they tied him on with ropes lest, in his delirium, he fall off. While doing this Nachi noticed the arrow sticking out of Cheis's arm. When he tried to remove it he found that the flint was too deeply embedded to budge, so he hacked off the shaft with his hunting knife.

"Show Chu-leh," Nachi said. "Go now." Chu-leh was a Chiricahua medicine man who specialized in curing arrow wounds.

Now Cheis embarked on a difficult journey. It was hard work

keeping the horses from running off, to say nothing of caring for the pain-crazed brave. But somehow he managed to get back to camp with all the horses. And Satl, though in great pain, was still alive when Cheis at last pulled up before the lodge of Chu-leh.

Together they carried Satl inside and laid him on a bed of cedar branches. After sprinkling him liberally with hoddentin, the medicine man brewed a drink of hot tea made with an infusion of herbs and grasses which he forced between the lips of the wounded brave.

All night long the monotonous sound of the drum and the chanted prayers of the medicine man sounded through the camp. In the morning Chu leh ordered a sweat bath for his patient. Satl recovered in a few days and eventually was able to go once again on the war path.

After helping Chu-leh care for Satl, Cheis had gone to the wickiup of his mother. When Naretena noticed his brother's swollen arm he urged Cheis to go to the medicine lodge of Chu-leh to have the arrowhead removed. Cheis refused, saying that Chu-leh was too busy caring for a wounded brave to be bothered with such a trifle as a flint embedded in the arm of a boy.

So Naretena took a sharp knife which had been in the loot captured from the Mexican wagon train. Lighting a small fire he heated the point in the coals. Without a word he cut into the upper arm of his brother and skillfully removed the flint. Then he bound up the wound with a piece of deerskin and tied it firmly with leather thongs.

"Be good, O Usen," Naretena said, as he sprinkled hoddentin on the bandaged arm, "and make well the arm of my brother, Child of the Water."

When Nachi and the braves returned with the flock of stolen sheep, there was great rejoicing in the camp. Although mutton was not as popular with the Chiricahuas as either the flesh of deer or antelope, and fell far below that of horse or mule meat, it was good to have a supply on hand.

Naretena's skill prompted Cheis to suggest that he become a medicine man like Chu-leh. Cheis had been dreading the time when Naretena would be old enough to start his novitiate—not because his young brother lacked bravery, but he was not strong enough to endure the rigors of warfare and raiding. If his brother became a medicine man he would not be expected to go on raids.

When Cheis spoke to his brother about this, Naretena said that he wished to become a "deer shaman," believing that he had the "deer ceremony." That was even better, thought Cheis. No opprobrium was attached to a man who failed to go on the warpath if he proved himself a good hunter, which anyone who possessed the "deer ceremony" was bound to be. Then, too, the Apaches believed that if a man who had the "deer ceremony" spent too much time on raids, he would lose his luck with deer.

To determine whether his brother really did possess the "deer ceremony," Cheis said that he was going hunting next day. So Naretena, after praying and singing over it for many hours, presented Cheis with a deer mask he had made. The prayers were sent directly to the animals themselves, instructing them to give their hides and meat to fill the needs of the Men of the Rising Sun.

On his hunt next day Cheis met with great success. He boasted all over the camp of his brother's "power," and many grown members of the tribe availed themselves of Naretena's ceremony, young though he was.

Ghost Face had come once more, and the lands of the Chiricahuas were held in its icy grip. The tribesmen sat in their wickiups making new weapons. The ever-busy squaws sewed moccasins and made apparel for their men. Many times during that winter Cheis went to one or another of the caves to bring the food stored there to feed the members of the tribe.

Cheis loved the long winter evenings, when he either played the moccasin game or listened to the stories the braves told of their exploits. He liked, too, to hear the braves tell of how they had acquired their names. The name of an Apache was a very valuable thing. Only under very special circumstances was it used. A person called by name was obliged to do whatever was asked of him. During a war or victory dance when a brave was called by name he must take part in the dance, and when an Apache was in trouble and called a man by name to help him, that man was honor-bound to come to his aid.

Apache warriors, though almost always given a name during their childhood, took their permanent names from some marked characteristic or because of some brave deed they had performed.

Cheis often wondered what his permanent name would be. Many of the tribe thought that Cheis suited him, for he was as hard and firm as wood, both in spirit and body. But Cheis longed to win a name by reason of a brave deed.

At last Ghost Face departed, and the first days of Little Eagles touched the land with warmth. It was time, Nachi thought, to organize another raid into Mexico. Although, thanks to the sheep taken from the Comanches, they still had plenty of jerked mutton and the hunters were bringing in deer and antelope nearly every day, the Chiricahuas wanted corn from which to brew tiswin. And the Mexicans had an abundance of corn stored in the small village of Tuape—theirs for the taking, so thought the Chiricahuas.

Once again Cheis and Pionsenay journeyed into the Sierra Madre Mountains, led by Nachi and the shaman Nan-ta-do-tash. Fifteen Chiricahua braves went on this trip, carrying huge burden baskets, woven by their squaws, in which to load the corn. This time they were mounted on the horses stolen on their last raid into Mexico. They did not plan to steal more horses unless, of course, a favorable opportunity presented itself, for at the time they had plenty. They did, however, need mules to carry the corn.

To protect their horses' feet from the sharp stones, the Chiricahuas cut pieces of rawhide into proper shapes, then soaked them from several days in water. This made the rawhide pliable. Then they fitted them onto the feet of the animals, drawing the tops around the fetlocks, and they were left on the horses' feet until they took form. After this they were removed to dry in the sun, then replaced. With these primitive horseshoes, traveling over the rough trails was much more comfortable for their steeds.

Mounted on his beautiful black stallion Intchi-dijin, Cheis rode happily along over the mountain passes and across the barren, cactus-covered plains.

Nachi and the six braves brought their rifles, which they had by now learned to use.

The braves camped outside the little village of Tuape, building no fire lest they warn the inhabitants of their presence.

At dawn the following morning—the favorite hour for an attack—Nachi painted stripes of white clay upon the faces and bodies of his braves. They believed this made them invisible to the enemy, and it gave them extra courage. Their enemies, too, believed that painted warriors had superhuman strength and luck. They feared them more than ever when they were so painted.

Full of confidence, the Chiricahuas stole silently into the village. Nachi divided his forces, sending half of them to attack the granary where the corn was stored, while some broke into the homes of the sleeping Mexicans, searching for loot. Still others waited outside the miserable hovels to kill or capture any who attempted to escape.

When the awakened Mexicans saw the painted, naked warriors breaking into their homes, they ran screaming outside. The looters grabbed whatever they could carry, then ran back to where Cheis and Pionsenay were waiting with the horses. As the Mexican men appeared outside their dwellings, they were bludgeoned to death by the war clubs of the Apaches. Some of the women were killed, too; others were taken captive with a score of small boys and girls.

These captives were taken to the novices to guard until the braves who were robbing the granary should complete their task and the journey back to their Stronghold could begin.

Soon the braves appeared with their great burden baskets filled with corn. But they still had no mules on which to transport it.

Nachi knew of a garrison of Mexican soldiers near this village where there were many mules shut up in corrals. Leaving Nan-ta-do-tash with Cheis and Pionsenay to guard the captives, Nachi and his braves mounted their horses and started for the barracks. They had already learned that most of the Mexican soldiers were away from their camp on a raid of their own. There would be, of course, a few soldiers left on guard. But even so, Nachi believed this was an opportune time to capture the mules.

From past experience the Chiricahuas knew that most Mexican soldiers were cowardly, and if their numbers were small they would speedily give up or else flee to try to save their miserable lives.

Galloping at top speed toward the barracks, they swept up to the corral, unfastened the gate and started rounding up the mules. A sleepy-eyed guard, seeing them, gave the alarm. Some of the soldiers, roused from their cots, fired a few shots at the marauders, killing two of the Chiricahuas. To the surprise of the Mexicans, who had never before seen Indians with rifles, Nachi and his six braves took aim, killing four soldiers outright and wounding two others. The rest ran screaming and cursing out of the barracks and made off into the near-by woods, leaving the field to the Chiricahua raiders.

Quickly herding the mules, they whipped their mounts and galloped back to the place where the shaman and the novices were waiting.

There they loaded the baskets of corn on the pack animals, and driving the thoroughly frightened captives before them they started back to the mountains. One little Mexican boy, less than two years old, cried so bitterly that Cheis leaned from his saddle and swept the child up off the ground, placing him on the saddle before him.

"Enju," said Nachi, when he saw his son's action. "That is good. We will make better time and get far away from the soldiers if we are not delayed by the captives who travel on foot." Then he ordered each of his braves to carry one or more children on his horse. As there was no room for the few Mexican women, the Apaches quickly dispatched them with their lances. Then they galloped off with their loot and captives.

On the return journey Nachi sent Cheis on ahead to scout, and Pionsenay and a young brave named Nolguin were told to stay several miles behind the main band and be on the lookout for pursuit. The Chiricahuas would not feel secure until they reached their own Stronghold, for should the raiding Mexican soldiers learn of the attack upon the barracks they would be sure to come after them.

Far in the lead, Cheis was alert for signs of the enemy.

Toward evening he saw the tracks of many horses in the sand of the mountain pass. Did that mean that the Mexican soldiers were ahead of them—planning to cut them off? He must find out, then send smoke signals to warn Nachi.

Cheis rode swiftly on. A short distance ahead he saw a company of twenty-five well-armed Mexican soldiers camped in a grove of hickory trees. Their horses were tethered some distance away, guarded by one indolent young Mexican.

Returning to a mountain ridge some miles back, Cheis gathered grass and leaves. Using his drill he made a small fire, adding sticks and branches of cedar until a column of smoke arose. Since he had nothing with which to spell out the dots and dashes of his message, he removed his breechclout and placed it again and again on the smoke so that the puffs multiplied rapidly. This warned his tribesmen that there was a large band of well-armed soldiers near by.

Then Cheis rode back toward the advancing Chiricahuas. They had read his message and left signs along the trail telling what direction they were taking. Where the trail forked he found a stick, its butt end pointing toward the west. Here and there along the way were stones so placed that he knew where to find the band. Once again he was grateful for the training he had received in his boyhood from Nah-kah-yen.

After following them for about half an hour, Cheis gave the hoot of an owl. Soon over the clear air came an answering call. And in a short while he came upon the band.

Reining in Intchi-dijin he rode up beside his father.

"Talk," his father ordered the boy.

"Twenty-five Mexican soldiers are camping in a grove of hickory trees five miles ahead," Cheis reported.

Nachi nodded.

That night the Chiricahuas made no camp, but pressed on

over the rough trail. They must make haste lest they be over-taken, for they had no wish to have a brush with those well-armed Mexican soldiers.

A great ambition burned in Cheis's breast. He wanted to return to the camp of the Mexican soldiers and capture their fine horses, but he was only a novice. He dared not make such a move without the consent of his chief. Yet how wonderful it would be to take that band of twenty-five splendid horses to the camp of the Men of the Rising Sun!

Again he sought out his father and rode silently beside him. On a raid a novice is not allowed to speak without a warrior's permission. For several miles, father and son rode side by side without a word.

Finally Nachi said, "You have something to say to me?"

Cheis told his father what was in his mind. He was in a fever of excitement as he awaited his father's answer.

At last Nachi drew rein and turned from the path, motioning Cheis to follow him. From a bag tied around his neck he took out his own tzi-daltai, sprinkled it with hoddentin and handed it to his son! Nachi's act showed Cheis more strongly than words how dangerous was the exploit he was to undertake. And it told, too, the depth of his father's love. For *never* does an Apache part with his tzi-daltai.

Elated, Cheis returned to a place about two miles east of the hickory grove. He dismounted, patted Intchi-dijin on the nose and went silently toward the camp of the soldiers.

The Mexicans were tired. They had ridden far that day. Then learning of the theft of the mules from their barracks, they had been obliged to take off after the thieves. Seeing no sign of the fugitive Indians they had decided to wait until day-light to hunt for them, meanwhile enjoying a much-desired rest.

As Cheis watched from the ridge above the camp, one after another of the soldiers fell asleep. Soon the guard, too, succumbed to fatigue.

Cautious as a cat, Cheis crept over the top of the ridge and down toward the sleeping camp. No dislodged stone, no snapping twig betrayed his movements. A falling feather would not have made less sound.

He went up to the horses, speaking softly to them. Speedily he cut both ends of the rope to which they were tethered. Catching one end of it in his hand he slowly led them out of the canyon.

Behind him the enemy soldiers slept on. Cheis almost laughed aloud as he pictured their dismay in the morning when they would find themselves afoot, many miles from any habitation.

Intchi-dijin stood faithfully waiting for his young master on the exact spot where Cheis had left him. Quickly mounting his horse he rode off to the Chiricahua Stronghold.

By nightfall of the next day, as he neared the camp of his people, he heard the voice of *es-a-da-ded*, the drum, the shouts of the men and the ululating cries of the squaws as they watched the warriors in the Victory Dance.

The loot had all been divided—the captive children allotted to the squaws who had few or no children of their own. The names of the two members of the tribe, killed by the Mexican soldiers, had been spoken for the last time, as Nachi told his people of their slaying. Never again would those names be mentioned in the camp of the Chiricahuas, for they considered it bad luck to say the name of the dead.

Cheis's mother Alope had looked in vain for her son among the returning heroes. Her eyes questioned Nachi but he paid no heed to her. But Naretena ran from one brave to another demanding to know what had happened to his brother. No one could tell him, for only Nachi knew what had kept Cheis from returning with the others. And Nachi would not speak.

Suddenly Cheis, mounted on Intchi-dijin and leading the string of twenty-five beautiful horses, rode into the camp. Four times around the fire he rode, then stopped proudly before his father, Chief Nachi. The drumbeats ceased; the cries were silenced as the people stared in amazement at the tall, lithe young brave upon the black horse.

Cheis leaped to the ground. He put the rope by which he had led the horses into his father's hand.

"Here are the horses, my father," he said, proudly. "I took them from the Mexican soldiers where they lay sleeping in a grove of hickory trees."

Nachi stepped forward. He put his hand on the shoulder of his brave young son.

"No more is your name Cheis, my son," he said in a vibrant voice. "Henceforth your name shall be Cochise—Hickory Wood."

"Cochise, Cochise," called the assembled people.
"Cochise, we say to you,
You! You!
We call you again and again."

Proudly Cochise stepped forward and took his place among the dancing warriors.

Chapter 6

New Chief of the Chiricahuas

AND NOW COCHISE WAS READY TO GO ON THE LAST RAID OF his novitiate, after which he could join in the battles of his people and sit in their councils. But many moons passed before Chief Nachi organized another raid. Meanwhile Cochise and his companions hunted deer and antelope, aided by the power of Naretena's "deer ceremony."

Another harvest, as Apaches called a year, rolled around before Cochise went on the last of his four raids. He was almost seventeen years old at this time, and had reached his full height of six feet, two inches—tall for an Apache. There was not an ounce of superfluous flesh on his strong body. Under his straight black hair his eyes were bright and clear and bold.

In many ways Cochise was a mystic. He believed profoundly in the religion of his people—in Usen, or Giver of Life; in Child of the Water, the son of White Painted Woman; in the Thunder People and in many lesser gans (as Apaches called their gods), who lived in the mountains.

Cochise often sat at the feet of the elders of the tribe, listening to their words, believing them to be endowed with wisdom. Savage though he was, Cochise possessed certain qualities rarely found except in the most civilized people. He always spoke the truth, having deep contempt for those who spoke with a "forked tongue."

Early in the summer of the year following their last raid, the Chiricahuas made one of their periodic pilgrimages from their Stronghold in the Dragoon Mountains to a favorite canyon in the Sierra Madres in what is now northern Mexico. Ever a nomadic people, they were constantly on the move from one camp to another. To them the Sierra Madres was a haven, where they rested after raids. These mountains rise from the desert to a great height—from cactus and heat to pine trees, live oaks and welcome coolness. The approach from Sonora was through almost impassable canyons.

Up these rocky heights the whole tribe would go—men, women and children, dogs, ponies and mules. There they would remain for months, secure in the shaded groves.

One day Nachi called his people together. From members of the tribe of the Coyotero Apaches who lived south of the Chiricahuas, he had heard strange tales. The Mexicans who lived in the village of Concurpe were feeling friendly toward the Apaches, and wished to trade blankets and trinkets for hides and furs. These rumors were worth investigating, Nachi thought, for although his braves always preferred to obtain their supplies by raid rather than trade, Nachi realized that on almost every raid some of his braves were killed and therefore his tribe was diminishing.

Mounted on some of the horses which Cochise had stolen from the Mexican soldiers, twelve braves journeyed toward the village of Concurpe. Three squaws went with them, a most unusual procedure, and one was Alope, Cochise's mother.

Before entering the village Nachi sent two scouts ahead to see if the stories of the Coyoteros were true, for it was hard to believe that Mexicans would ever be on friendly terms with Apaches.

On their return the scouts reported that many wagonloads of goods had just been received in the village which the inhabitants were eager to trade for furs. They said, too, that the Mexicans were planning a feast that day, that their women had cooked much food and brewed much liquor. Also they had seen some Coyotero braves wandering about the streets of the town—unharmed.

Nachi consulted Tagj-sa-ta, the shaman in charge of this expedition. He, in turn, consulted his "power," who assured him that it would be safe for the Men of the Rising Sun to venture into the village of Concurpe.

The Chiricahua did not enter the village in a body, for fear the Mexicans might misinterpret their friendly intent. Singly, or in pairs, the braves with their squaws showed themselves on the streets. They wore no paint nor any other symbol of warfare and had left all their weapons in their hiding place—together with their horses—under the eyes of the shaman and Cochise's brother Juan, who was just starting to become a war novice. Of course each brave had a sharp-edged knife hidden in the folds of his moccasins—for never was an Apache completely unarmed.

On the streets of Concurpe they met many Mexicans who

greeted them cordially, calling them "amigos" (friends). The alcalde (mayor) himself invited them to a feast in the large town hall.

With almost childlike confidence the Chiricahuas entered the hall. At one end musicians sat playing guitars, zithers and drums. The Mexicans offered their guests seats on the benches lined along the walls, but unused to such things, however, they squatted upon the floor.

Something about all this rang false to both Cochise and Alope. They refused to eat the food and drink the liquor, which was served so liberally by their Mexican hosts. It was strange that Cochise, the youngest of the braves, should be the only one there who doubted the sincerity of the Mexicans' hospitality.

All the other Apaches were having a riotous good time, smacking their lips over the spicy Mexican food and washing it down with great quaffs of tiswin. Before long the braves— Nachi among the rest—were completely befuddled. Some of them were even stretched out on the floor in a drunken sleep.

Then the treacherous Mexicans turned on the Indians with knives, lances and war clubs, killing or wounding them right and left. Cochise and Alope were everywhere at once, tugging at their inert tribesmen, trying to rouse them from their drink-induced lethargy. As Alope bent over the prone body of her husband, a Mexican started toward her, knife in hand.

But her alert son saw this just in time. Grabbing a war club he swung it at the head of the Mexican, who fell to the floor— dead.

Though badly wounded, Nachi was still alive. They must get him away quickly. Putting his strong hands under his father's shoulders, Cochise dragged his limp body to the door, while Alope covered their retreat with a rifle she had picked up from one of the benches. Fortunately the other Mexicans were engaged in mutilating the bodies of the Apaches they had killed, and were unaware of what Cochise and his mother were doing.

They left the hall. Luck was with them, for a pair of saddled and bridled horses were tethered outside the door. Together Cochise and Alope lifted Nachi, tying him on the back of one of the horses. Then, still armed with the rifle, Alope mounted the other horse. Cochise jumped up behind her. Alope took the reins, giving Cochise the rifle.

When they heard shots behind them they knew that their departure had not been unnoticed after all. How far would they be pursued? Cochise wondered. The rifle held just one shot, and except for the knife in the pocket of his moccasin he was totally unarmed.

Soon he saw two mounted Mexicans pounding along the road behind them. Turning in his saddle and taking careful aim, Cochise pulled the trigger. He missed the Mexican but hit the horse, killing it. As his mount fell, its rider tumbled off, badly hurt.

But the other pursuer came galloping toward them. He had already fired the one shot in his own rifle. So he, too, was unarmed except for his spear, which he threw as he came closer. It missed both Cochise and Nachi, but lodged in the body of the horse which was carying the all but lifeless body of the chief. The animal reared and uttered a terrified scream before it fell dead.

Cochise drew rein, while Alope leaped from the saddle and untied the body of her husband from the dead horse. Cochise, too, dismounted, placing his horse as a barrier in front of Nachi and his mother.

The Mexican came on. Soon they would be utterly at his mercy. He dared not let the Mexican get too close, for he well knew that they would be run down under the hoofs of the horse.

Cochise stood facing the Mexican, his knife in his hand. "Be good, O Usen," he prayed soundlessly. "Let me kill my enemy."

Taking aim, he hurled the knife at his adversary. It whizzed through the air, striking the Mexican in the throat.

Apparently there were no other pursuers. Alope and Cochise tied Nachi on the back of the horse they had been riding. While her son held his father on its back, Alope led the horse to the grove where Tagj-sa-ta and Juan waited.

They quickly told of the Mexicans' treachery, while the shaman examined the wounds of their chief. Tagj-sa-ta said they must return at once to their camp where Chu-leh would make medicine to heal Nachi's wounds. For he did not have the "power" and the spirits would work against them if he tried.

When they reached their camp Cochise related the terrible story of what had occurred in the village of Concurpe. There was great wailing as the widows of the ten slain warriors learned of the death of their husbands. Three children of the murdered squaws were left motherless, but they were immediately adopted by other women of the tribe, for no matter how fierce and cruel he might be when on the warpath, the Apache was kindly at home. Children were dearly loved by both men and women, and always well cared for.

Because he was the chief, other medicine men besides Chu-leh were called in to help with Nachi's cure. Through the three days and nights that followed, the sound of the beating drum and the chanting of the shamans was heard throughout the camp. Between the chanting, the medicine men applied pollen to Nachi's forehead, then in the form of a cross upon his breast, then around the bed of cedar boughs on which he lay.

As the days and nights passed without their patient's showing any signs of improvement, all the shamans of the tribe conferred—whatever their special curing power might be—each suggesting a different treatment.

Finally they decided to hold a dance for the wounded chief in order to drive away the maleficent spirits who were preventing Nachi's recovery. But though the shamans danced and stamped and howled around the bed of the sufferer, nothing availed. Without regaining consciousness, Nachi, chief of the Chiricahuas, died during the fifth night following his return.

Next morning at dawn the whole camp went into mourning. Nachi's wives cut their hair, blackened their faces and donned ragged clothes. Dressed in his finest garments, the body of the chief was taken to a cave far away in the mountains to be buried. As the funeral procession passed the wickiups in which the squaws and children must stay while the burial was in progress—for the Apaches did not allow them to be present at the tomb of the dead—they cried and wailed pitifully.

Soon after Nachi's death, the tribe left that camp, having first burned all the wickiups they had occupied. They returned to the Stronghold in the Dragoon Mountains, where Cochise had been born and which was to remain his favorite haunt all of his life. Here the women erected new wickiups, and the life of the camp was quickly resumed. Nachi's name was never again spoken by his people. Although Cochise, too, never mentioned his father, he grieved deeply, for great love and trust had existed between them.

Four days after their arrival at the new camp, Cochise called the warriors together. "I go to avenge what was done to our people by the treacherous Mexicans," he said. "Who will ride with me?"

Every able-bodied man in the camp responded. They sharpened their lances and put fresh feathers on their arrows. They treated the arrowheads with poison made from the sharp prongs of prickly pear cactus pounded in animals' blood which had been allowed to spoil.

Even though every adult male capable of fighting had enlisted, Cochise believed they might need more warriors if they were to wipe out the entire population of Concurpe as they had vowed to do. To summon their neighbors, the Mimbreños, they lit signal fires on the mountaintops. The fires burned in a steady flame by night and rose in a straight column of smoke by day.

Mangas Coloradas, great chief of the Mimbreños, arrived with fifty fighting men. Mangas was a mighty man—tall and broad, with an enormous head and small, though piercing and intelligent, eyes. He was twenty years older than Cochise, but already there was a bond of love and respect between them.

He had ample reason to hate the Mexicans. They had killed his father and mother and other members of his family, after days of the most cruel torture. Mangas had avenged their death many times, and he was more feared and hated by the Mexicans than any Apache in the land. It was the Mexicans who had given him his name—Mangas Coloradas (Red Sleeves)—because of his habit of bathing his great arms in the blood of his victims.

When Mangas learned of the perfidy of the Mexicans he readily agreed to take part in the battle, placing himself and his fifty braves at the disposal of Cochise. Nor did he presume either on his years or superior experience to dictate to the young Chiricahuan. This expedition had been called by the eldest son of the chief. He would lead it. Mangas would follow.

This was the first of many times that Mangas Coloradas of the Mimbreños and Cochise of the Chiricahuas took the war-path together.

The night before the war party was to leave they staged one of the fiercest dances the tribe had ever held.

They arrived at the adobe houses of the village of Concurpe before dawn. This time they sought no loot. They carried off no captives. This was a fight to the death. With lances and war clubs they attacked the sleeping Mexicans and wrought a terrible punishment. They spared no one and they believed they had killed the entire population of the town. But four of the Mexicans were still alive when the Apaches rode off, although only one of them was not wounded.

He rallied sufficiently to ride post haste to the nearest barracks and rouse the soldiers, who quickly armed and took off after the fleeing Apaches.

And now the young Chiricahuan demonstrated the leadership and strategy he was often to display in the years to come. When they had put about twenty miles between themselves and the village of Concurpe, Cochise became aware that soldiers of the enemy were hot on their trail and would soon be close enough to use their rifles. He ordered two of the ablest Chiricahua scouts to stay behind and show themselves to the enemy. Then the braves, both the Chiricahuas and the Mimbreños, hid themselves among the great boulders of the roughest places they could find in the mountain pass.

Already well within the range of the guns of the enemy, the two scouts feigned ignorance of the approaching Mexicans. As they moved toward the place where their companions were hiding, the scouts watched sharply, preparing to run as soon as the soldiers shot at them. When the first bullets came whizzing toward them, the scouts rushed toward their own comrades. The soldiers of the enemy followed directly behind the two decoys, and were met by the Apaches who dealt swift death to many of them. The others turned and fled back to the safety of their barracks.

Mangas Coloradas watched Cochise's strategy. Like a true Apache he allowed no words of praise to pass his lips, but his eyes glowed with admiration. He recognized in Cochise a man of great promise, at once brave, strong and wise.

Riding night and day, the Apaches pressed on until they reached their Stronghold in the Dragoons. Even after so marked a victory there was no dance of celebration at the camp upon their return. The people's grief over the death of their beloved chief was too fresh in their hearts for that.

The days passed. Mangas and his warriors returned to their own lands. As Cochise walked about the camp of his tribe, the braves looked at him speculatively but with admiration in their eyes.

One day Naretena and Cochise were walking alone through the forest.

"There is talk, my brother," the younger boy said.

"What talk?" Cochise demanded.

"The braves say it is time to elect a new chief for the Men of the Rising Sun, now that he is gone." This was the closest the boy dared come to speaking of the death of his father, for the word "dead" must never be spoken by an Apache. "They say," Naretena continued, "that the eldest son, young though he is, should be made chief."

Cochise made no reply, but his excitement was great. For the first time since Nachi's death joy filled his heart. He, at eighteen, chief of the Chiricahuas? He, the leader of his people? Could it be true?

Naretena was right. In a few days a meeting was called, attended by the headmen, the subchiefs, the shamans as well as all the adult men and women of the tribe. Even old Tze-ge-juni, the medicine woman who had officiated at Cochise's birth, was present.

The meeting lasted four days, the first one given over to feasting. On the second day, they heard from one after another of the warriors who had accompanied Cochise on his war of vengeance into Mexico. They told of his bravery, his cleverness. They recounted the exploit that had earned him his name. They told of the skill he had displayed in leading the pursuing Mexican soldiers into ambush and slaughtering them on their return from the village of Concurpe.

Then spoke Nan-ta-do-tash, most honored of all the shamans. "For three hundred harvests," he said, "the forefathers of this youth have been leaders of the Men of the Rising Sun. This would mean nothing if he himself were not worthy. True, he is young, but he has displayed wisdom beyond his years. He is strong and brave, and never does he speak with a forked tongue. He is fit to be the successor of the mighty men who have gone before him." Nan-ta-do-tash paused and looked around the circle of warriors. "What say you, my braves?"

"Enju—it is well," grunted the braves in unison.

But two days more elapsed before Cochise was notified that he had been elected chief. He was not present on the day when his virtues had been extolled, but Naretena was and he repeated it all to his elder brother.

Cochise went alone to the high peak, where he had stood all night before going on his first raid. This time he prayed to Usen for strength and wisdom to be a fit leader of his people.

High in the air above him an eagle flew across the sky, its scream ringing in Cochise's ears. He clutched his tzi-daltai in his hand and placed it upon his heart as he made obeisance to Usen.

On the fourth day of the meeting, Nan-ta-do-tash ordered a sweat bath for all the braves. Then Cochise was summoned before the warriors and told that he had been chosen their chief. Cochise wore no special uniform, no insignia except a war charm bandoleer. This consisted of four strands of buckskin twisted together. On it was tied an eagle feather, which represented holy words. There were also turquoise and pieces of obsidian fastened on it to represent the xal—the mythical weapon with which Child of the Water had killed the four monsters.

As Nan-ta-do-tash put the bandoleer around Cochise's shoulders, he spoke these words which the new chief repeated after him.

"I call on sky and on earth. Bats will fly, turning upside down with me in battle. Black sky will enfold me and protect my body and earth will do likewise."

And so Cochise became chief of the Chiricahuas.

Chapter 7

Marriage

ON THE HIGHEST PEAK OF THE MOUNTAINS TO THE EAST OF the Stronghold a signal fire was burning. A steady column of smoke rising into the azure sky signaled "Come." Chief Cochise sent Pionsenay to the camp of the Mimbreños to learn why they were being summoned.

"Chief Mangas Coloradas invites all the Men of the Rising Sun and their squaws and children to the puberty rite of his sister Tesalbestinay," Pionsenay reported upon his return. "He especially wants the chief of the Chiricahuas to attend. Tesalbestinay is very beautiful," Pionsenay added slyly.

"Enju," Cochise responded. "We will go. Mangas Coloradas

is our good brother. Never have the Mimbreños taken the warpath against our people. Carry back this message. Say that we will come with glad hearts."

Then Cochise told his tribe about the forthcoming ceremony, bidding all who wished to attend to make ready to leave next morning.

The puberty rite—or maturation ceremony—is the most important event in the life of an Apache woman. It is held to celebrate her coming of age. In one way it resembles the coming-out party of an American debutante, for it announces that she is ready for marriage.

The Chiricahua squaws packed their burden baskets with gifts of food: fresh deer and antelope meat; cakes of mescal; blossoms of the locust tree; chokeberries, mulberries and a special one-seeded nut of the juniper tree, which grew in the Stronghold of the Chiricahuas and nowhere else throughout all Apacheria.

The puberty rite offered a social good time as well as a ritual. There would be dancing and feasting. Presents would be exchanged. Therefore many of the squaws joined the procession that left on foot the following morning. Some carried babies in cradleboards slung upon their backs.

When they reached the Mimbreño camp they found that the maturation ceremony for Tesalbestinay, sister of the great Mangas Coloradas, was to begin next day.

At sunrise the Singer, who played an important role in the ceremony, asked the male members of Testalbestinay's family to erect the ceremonial lodge in which the girl would stay during the four days. The men lifted the poles of spruce, placing the ends into the holes especially prepared for them. As they were set in place, the Singer chanted special songs of the four stallions which the poles symbolized. He sang of the Killer of

Enemies, brother of Child of the Water, and the long life for which the blue, the yellow, the black and the white stallions stood.

Like everything in Apache rituals, the number four was sacred, and the four colors referred to the corners of the compass —blue for the south, yellow for the west, white for the north and black for the east.

After the ceremonial lodge was built, the Mimbreño squaws appeared with bowls filled with mesquite beans, boiled meats, baked mescal and yucca fruit. There bowls were placed before the entrance of the lodge in a line from east to west. Then the Singer sprinkled them with sacred pollen, and everyone gathered around to feast.

After eating, the structure was then completed. It was considered the home of White Painted Woman—the Madonna of the Apaches—and for the four days of the rites, Tesalbestinay *was* White Painted Woman and was called by that name.

As the girl entered the ceremonial lodge, the Singer, accompanying his song with shuffling dance steps, intoned these words:

> "Killer of Enemies, source of long life,
> White Painted Woman has come inside;
> She grows up by means of it."

A skin was placed on the ground before the lodge upon which Tesalbestinay knelt. She was dressed in a beautiful robe of freshly tanned buckskin. The dress had a yellow background, the color of hoddentin. It was decorated with designs symbolizing the forces which would be supplicated in the girl's behalf—the morning star and the crescent moon; circles representing the sun, with silver rays streaming out from the centers and gorgeously painted arcs depicting the rainbow.

Her Attendant, an older woman whom Tesalbestinay had chosen to serve her during the ceremony, then marked the girl's cheeks with pollen.

Many times throughout the ceremony the Attendant uttered a high-pitched cry—like the cry of applause which greeted the returning braves after a successful raid. The Apaches believed that this cry was first used by White Painted Woman when her son returned after slaying the four monsters.

During the ceremony the girl was supposed to have power to heal the sick and to bring good luck to all who appealed to her.

The first of the many members of the tribe who went into the ceremonial lodge to receive the maiden's blessing was an old squaw, gnarled and twisted with rheumatism. In a cracked voice, she sang:

"I come to White Painted Woman,
  By means of long life I come to her.
  I come to her by means of her blessing,
  I come to her by means of her good fortune.
  I come to her by means of all her different fruits.
  By means of the long life she bestows, I come to her;
  By means of the holy truth she goes about."

In her role of White Painted Woman, Tesalbestinay placed her strong young hands on the body of the supplicant. As the old squaw stumbled out of the lodge there was a light of ecstasy on her wrinkled face.

One after another the Mimbreño men, women and children entered the ceremonial wickiup to receive the blessing of "White Painted Woman." Even some of the Chiricahuas entered the lodge. One of these was Cochise. The young chief was struck by the girl's beauty. Her brown eyes were as gentle as a doe's. Her face, though strong, had an almost mystic radiance.

A strange sensation came er him as Tesalbestinay put her hands upon the wound made by the Comanche arrow at the time of his second raid. After putting her hands on his arm, she held it to her breast, bowing her head over it.

"You will have a long life," Tesalbestinay said softly, her eyes dropping before the ardor in his. "All good things will be yours. The rays of Holos will warm you. The rain will cool you. The nights will bring you rest. Your days on earth will be as bright as the stars in the heavens."

They entertained themselves with dancing, singing and games and racing followed in the afternoon. All that time Tesalbestinay stayed quietly within the lodge.

Cochise took no part in these social activities either. Finding a quiet nook far away from the others, he sat and brooded. He knew that his tribe expected him to marry and father children. What better mate could he find than this beautiful sister of the great chief of the Mimbreños?

All the young unmarried Mimbreño braves looked longingly at Tesalbestinay. Also many of the married men desired to take her for their second, third or even fourth wife, for not only was she strong and beautiful, she was the sister of their great and powerful chief.

But Cochise wanted her, too, for he had fallen in love with her. He went to the wickiup of her brother. After the two Chiefs had settled themselves on blankets and sat silently regarding one another for some time, Apache fashion, Cochise said, "I wish to tie my horses before the wickiup of your sister."

Cochise was referring to the Indian way of asking for the hand of a maiden in marriage. In the night the suitor tethered horses before the wickiup of the parents of the girl whom he wished to marry. The number and quality of the horses indicated to the girl's family both the extent of his worldly possessions and the degree of his ardor. She was permitted four days to reach a decision. It was not considered good form for her to care for the animals the first day. Such action would stamp her as being immodest. On the other hand, if she allowed the full four days to elapse before she fed and watered them it showed her to be vain and proud. If she paid no attention to them whatsoever, the lover knew that his suit was rejected.

There was deep affection in Mangas's face as he regarded the young chief, for he loved Cochise best of all Apache chieftains. He was delighted that his sister had found favor in Cochise's eyes. Besides, such a marriage would cement the relationship between the Mimbreños and the Chiricahuas—an excellent thing in time of war.

Mangas knew, of course, that since Cochise was a chieftain, the usual custom among Apaches—that of the bridegroom's going to live with the family of his bride and becoming a member of her tribe—could not be followed. But the camps of the Chiricahuas and the Mimbreños were not far apart. He would be able to see his well-loved sister often. And although Cochise would not be forced to support his wife's people, as Apache bridegrooms must do, Mangas knew the generous young Chiricahuan would be good to them.

"My sister shares the wickiup of my first wife and our two sons," Mangas said.

"I will tie my horses there tonight," said Cochise.

"Enju," responeded Mangas. "It is well."

So that night Cochise tied his beloved horse Intchi-dijin, together with three others almost equally good, before the wickiup of Placid, eldest of the wives of Mangas Coloradas.

From inside the wickiup Tesalbestinay saw what Cochise was doing and thrilled at the sight. For she, like Cochise, had felt a wave of love and wonder sweep through her when first they looked at one another.

Tesalbestinay found it hard to wait a whole day before caring for Cochise's horses. But she must not appear too forward to the members of her tribe, even though it was the handsome young chief of the Chiricahuas who wooed her.

She was up very early next morning, however. Stealing silently out of the wickiup, she led the four beautiful horses to the creek to drink. Then she fed them great bunches of rich grama grass that grew near by.

From the wickiup which he shared with some of the members of his own tribe, Cochise saw this. A great glow of happiness and peace swept through him. Later in the morning he managed to meet his beloved in a sheltered place far from the eyes of both the Mimbreños and the Chiricahuas.

"I must go back to my home to build our bridal wickiup," he said with shining eyes. "I will return as soon as possible for our marriage feast. Will you wait for me?"

"Until Holos gives no heat and the waters of the river cease to flow, I will wait," Tesalbestinay whispered softly.

So Cochise returned to the encampment of his people, high in the Dragoon Mountains. He sought a secluded spot close by a rushing mountain stream, where great trees met overhead and flowers and ferns grew underfoot. There he built a temporary wickiup for the week which he and his bride would spend together. He brought skins of mountain lions he had killed for their bed, and stocked the dwelling with fine foods from his mother's larder. When all was in readiness he returned to the camp of the Mimbreños.

Now that Cochise had been accepted, Mangas arranged a

great feast in honor of the bridal pair. For three days the celebration continued, but Cochise and Tesalbestinay were not
allowed to speak to one another the whole time, nor be alone
together even for a moment.

On the third day, however, they suddenly disappeared.
Mounted on a dun-colored stallion as fleet and beautiful as
Intchi-dijin, with his bride seated postilion fashion behind him,
clinging to his strong shoulders, Cochise galloped away from
the camp of the Mimbreños.

Cochise and Tesalbestinay spent a happy week in their
bridal wickiup, learning to know each other, sharing one another's thoughts and falling even deeper in love.

When the week was over, Cochise tore down the wickiup and
led his bride to the center of the encampment of his own people,
where Tesalbestinay, like every good Apache squaw, built a
new home for her lord, assuming the responsibilities and per-
forming all the heavy labors of her kind.

She knew that her husband undoubtedly would marry other
squaws as the years passed, but she did not mind this. He
would be a poor provider, indeed, were he not able to support
more than one wife. Besides, with other wives to help, her own
burdens would be lightened. But all this was in the future. For
the present they were alone. Cochise was all hers now, and she
was very happy.

Throughout the camp of the Chiricahuas, many a maiden
nursed an aching heart as she watched Cochise with his bride,
for every one of them longed to be the chosen wife of the
wonderful young chief. But they accepted Tesalbestinay and
treated her well, although no one said a word of welcome to her.

Naretena, alone, showed his joy because of the new-found
happiness of his beloved elder brother.

Chapter 8

First Treachery of the White Eyes

SOMETIMES when Cochise and his braves were on a raid or out hunting, they saw small parties of white men. Some of them were trappers, who took beaver from the sparse streams in the lands of the Apaches. Cochise could understand them. But he could not make out those other men, whom he called "rock scratchers," who hunted with their picks and shovels in the mountains and river beds for "yellow iron," as the Apaches called gold. Why did they want it? It could not be eaten; it was too soft to be used for weapons—and it certainly could not keep them warm in winter or cool during the burning days of summer.

Except that their loud-voiced weapons sometimes frightened away the game, these men did no harm, so far as Cochise could see. Compared with the treacherous Mexicans, the white men offered no threat to the peace of the tribes. Like true Apaches, the Chiricahuas did not show themselves to the "White Eyes," as they called the Americans.

Although very few of them had come into Cochise's country, he learned from Mangas Coloradas, a part of whose lands lay in the territory known as the "Copper Mines," which had formerly been worked by the Mexicans, that there were many of the White Eyes there. They searched for "white iron" (silver) as well as for gold. That these strange men, with hair all over their faces, set such store by these things was as great a puzzle to Mangas as it was to Cochise.

Though each of the many tribes had its own chief, in those days there was a great head chief of all the Apaches. This was Juan José. When Juan was a little boy his father, Chief Tulac, had sent him to a Spanish priest to be educated in a mission school. There he had been given his Spanish name. Chief Tulac had promised the priest that Juan would grow up to be a "man of God."

But in the year 1805, when Juan was a young man, the Mexicans killed his father after prolonged torture. After this, when Juan became chief of all the Apaches he forgot about being a "man of God," and swore death to all Mexicans. In the thirty-odd years that followed, Juan José had made good that threat whenever he could. The depredations he committed throughout Sonora—and what is now Arizona—spread terror among the Mexicans.

Juan José was neither a great warrior nor was he wise in council. Nonetheless, he was as much a ruler of the Apache tribes as those thoroughly independent people ever had. Each tribe gave him a certain amount of deference—it could hardly be called obedience.

But over the years Juan José had grown fat and lazy. Even his former hatred of the Mexicans had abated somewhat. Early in the century he had been foolish enough to allow some Mexicans to resume work at the Copper Mines. Had he not permitted this, many pages of the history of the Southwest would read differently.

In the year 1837 the Mexicans of both the states of Sonora and Chihuahua were at war with the Apaches. They had become tired of the constant raiding. That year the government of Chihuahua put forth a law called "Proyecto de Guerre" or "Project of War," by which the state offered one hundred dollars for the scalp of an Apache warrior, fifty dollars for the scalp of a squaw, and twenty-five dollars for a child's. This gave the Mexicans an added incentive to kill Apaches. And the Apaches, of course, became more bloodthirsty than ever in their treatment of the Mexicans. Even Juan José became more warlike.

But the Americans had nothing to fear at the hands of Juan José, for he had always been friendly toward them.

One of the white men who had penetrated into the lands of the Apaches was a certain James Johnson, a trader at Oposure, whom the Apaches called "Don Santiago." Juan José believed this trader to be his very good friend. He liked the presents Johnson brought him: blankets, maize, beads, knives, coffee—and especially wine. The white men who came into his country to trap beaver or hunt for gold and silver did not intend to overrun it, Juan believed. When they had found sufficient yellow iron or beaver furs they would pack them on the backs of their mules and go back to their own country.

Unknown to Juan José, Johnson wished to profit by the bounty given by the Mexican government for Apache scalps.

"Why bother to sell the fur of animals, which is harder to get, when one can make easy money by selling Apache hair?" he argued. Nor was the rascal always scrupulous about making sure that the hair came from the heads of Apaches. Sometimes he and others of his kind killed and scalped the peaceful Pima and Maricopa Indians—always friends of the white men— and occasionally even the Mexicans themselves. "The stupid Mexican government would never know the difference." Johnson said. "Hair is hair."

One morning Juan José came out of his wickiup and saw, in the distance, little clouds of dust on the trail of the foothills of the Mongollons.

"Horsemen are coming," he said to Adala, one of his wives. "Maybe they are White Eyes, friends of our good Don Santiago. He has told me much about his people. They are good and wise, and there are many of them—more than all the Mexicans and Apaches combined."

But the horseman Juan had seen was not his friend Santiago Johnson. It was Mangas Coloradas, the Mimbreño chief. With him was a Mexican prisoner, bound and tied.

"Why did you not kill this Mexican?" Juan demanded of Mangas. "Our people kill all Mexicans who buy Apache scalps."

Mangas explained that he had seen the Mexican giving Don Santiago a piece of paper. He had brought him here to tell his story to Juan José before killing him.

The Mexican said the paper bore a message from the governor of Sonora, saying he would pay Don Santiago Johnson five thousand pesos if he would kill the chief of the Apaches—Juan José; and that he would pay one hundred pesos for each Apache warrior killed and ten pesos for each woman and child.

"What did Don Santiago say?" Juan José demanded.

"He said that he would do it," the Mexican answered, cringing before the wrath in the eyes of the chief.

"You speak with a forked tongue," Juan José's voice rose in fury. "Don Santiago is my friend. Neither he nor any American has ever broken faith with me, nor I with them. Kill this lying Mexican," he ordered.

When next Juan José saw his "friend" Johnson, he told the trader what the Mexican had said.

Johnson gave a loud guffaw. "That message was only about some mules that the governor of Sonora wants to buy," he said. "Someday soon I will visit your camp with some of my American friends who live in the United States in a place called Missouri. They want to buy some of your mules, too, and I will help them."

"Enju," said the chief. "Our people will have a big feast for our American friends."

A month later Johnson sent word to Juan José that he and his friends would be with them in two days' time, with a wagon-load of presents. Juan ordered the squaws to prepare food for the White Eyes. There were only six warriors in Juan's camp that day, for the others had gone off into the mountains to hunt. But these decked themselves out in their finest buckskin garments for the feast. The women and children having first scrubbed in a near-by stream, dressed in their cleanest clothes. Mangas came bringing his wife Placid and some of his children. Everyone was happily awaiting the arrival of the Americans.

On the second day Johnson arrived with a party of nine trappers. With him, too, was a thin, narrow-eyed man named Gleason. Johnson brought a wagon which the Apaches believed contained the promised presents.

Toward sunset after their arrival, Johnson, with Gleason's help, piled some sacks of pinole (corn) before his tent. On top of the corn-filled sacks they placed strings of beads, bolts of calico and other gifts dear to the hearts of Apache squaws.

But under the sacks was hidden an old-fashioned blunderbuss, loaded with bits of rusty chain, pieces of scrap iron, lead balls and broken glass. Neither the trappers—who were innocent of this ghastly crime about to be committed—nor the happy Apaches noticed the white cotton wick, which was a fuse leading to a powder charge, sticking out from one of the sacks.

Johnson, all smiles, played host to the Apaches, bidding them come forward to receive their presents. The six warriors stood far back from the sacks, for this was squaw's business. Juan José, standing under a cottonwood tree at the edge of the crowd, looked on, smiling benignly. Johnson, with a long lighted cigar in his mouth, was behind the sacks of corn.

Gleason tried to urge Juan José to hand out the gifts to the women and children, but the chief said that since they were presents from Don Santiago it was more fitting that he distribute them.

Then Gleason, seeing that this strategy had failed, said, "Don Santiago Johnson tells me you have a good saddle mule which maybe you will sell me. Let me see it. If it is as good as he says it is, I'll buy it from you."

Juan was proud of his mule and eager to show it off to this man—the friend of his great "friend" Don Santiago. He proudly led the treacherous American to the corral where the mule was tethered.

Just then Johnson touched the glowing end of his cigar to the fuse. There was a terrific roar. Thunder burst from the earth. The plaza became littered with the hacked and chopped bodies of Apache women and children. Blood spilled over their clean clothes.

With that, Gleason drew his pistol and put a bullet into the back of the Apache chief, who had turned to stroke his mule. But the bullet only wounded him. Juan jumped at Gleason, knocking him to the ground. He whipped out his knife but hesitated to use it.

When Johnson saw Gleason's predicament he came running toward them.

"Don Santiago," cried Juan José, "your friend tried to kill me. I can kill him now, but I don't want to kill an American, especially your friend. If you promise to protect me, I will let him live."

But Johnson answered by firing his pistol at the Apache chief, killing him. Gleason sprang from under Juan's dead body and he and Johnson rushed to their horses, which were saddled and ready for a rapid retreat. They fled west toward the Gila River, leaving behind the camp of the Apaches turned into a shambles. Twenty women and children lay dead. More were badly wounded. The piteous voices of dying children, crying to their dead mothers, sounded throughout the camp.

The sun, red as the lifeblood of the victims, slipped behind the western hills, as though trying to hide its face from such perfidy.

The six Apache warriors who had held back from the "present giving," and had therefore escaped injury from the blast, did not know that the nine trappers from Missouri were innocent of this outrage. They hurried to their wickiups and returned with lances and hunting knives. All but two of the trappers, who managed to escape, were killed.

Among the butchered Apaches lay the dead body of Mangas Coloradas' wife Placid and three of his children. Only his son Chie escaped the cruel death.

Thus opened the Apache warfare upon Americans.

Within an hour after the slaughter, Mimbreño Apaches were carrying the news of the massacre, gathering together all of Juan's fighting men to make war on the Americans whenever and wherever found.

Later a war council was called at the camp of Mangas Coloradas, which was attended by the chiefs of many tribes throughout Apacheria.

Cochise and many other braves of the Chiricahuas came to the council.

With the death of Juan José, the title of chief of all the Apaches died, too, never to be revived. Some Apaches wanted Mangas to assume leadership, but many others preferred Cochise, young though he was. So the two men talked it over and divided the territory between them—Cochise dominating the western part and Mangas the land to the east.

Many years before, when on a raid into Mexico, Mangas Coloradas had captured a beautiful young Mexican woman, making her his third wife. This woman, Ana, gave birth to three daughters as lovely as herself. The sagacious Mimbreño cemented the bonds of friendship with some of the other tribes by marrying Ana's eldest daughter to the chief of the Navahos, her second daughter to the chief of the White Mountain Apaches, while the third became the wife of the chief of the Coyoteros. And, of course, his own sister Tesalbestinay was already the wife of Cochise of the Chiricahuas. Thus Mangas made allies of many tribes throughout Apacheria.

One time, shortly after the massacre at the camp of Juan José, Mangas took his young son Chie, whose mother had been killed in the terrible slaughter, to Cochise's encampment.

"This ish-kay-nay" said Mangas, "is a strange one. The fire wagons of the White Eyes could not touch him. For he pushed himself up from the ground and would not be left for dead, though all about him lay the dead and dying. In the camp of my brother some value may be found in him."

"Enju," Cochise answered. "It will be good to have the son of my brother in our camp."

And so Chie, the son of Mangas Coloradas, went to live in the wickiup of Cochise and Tesalbestinay, and became a companion to their own little son, born a year before.

In their many meetings in the years that followed, Cochise of the Chiricahuas and Mangas Coloradas of the Mimbreños held many talks about the white men. Both chiefs shared an interest in these strange creatures, often tinged with admiration, even after the treachery perpetrated at the camp of Juan José.

The years rolled on and the enmity of the Apaches toward the few white Americans who invaded their lands was almost equal to their hatred for the Mexicans. Perfectly acquainted with their lands, knowing every spring, waterhole and canyon for hundreds of miles around, they had a great advantage over the Americans, who knew nothing of the country. Apaches could travel on foot over the roughest terrain for fifty to seventy-five miles a day, and had sufficient endurance to keep up this pace for days. They carried few provisions, for even in that arid country an Apache could always find something to eat. From their remote and almost inaccessible hide-outs, they spied on the white men. Through smoke signals they were able to communicate with each other and still keep themselves hidden. They rarely fought in the open or against a well-armed force. And when they were sometimes hard pressed, they scattered and disappeared like a flock of quail—to meet again at some prearranged spot.

But for a short time this enmity between Apaches and white men ceased. For, to their great surprise, the Apaches learned that the Americans were at war with their own bitter enemies—the Mexicans. On a certain day, when Cochise was with Mangas at the latter's camp, a party of white soldiers, led by the American, General Kearney, appeared, leading a train consisting of pack mules.

"I have come," the general said to Mangas Coloradas, "to trade for mules with our Apache friends. We need these mules to help us make war on your enemies to the south, who are now our enemies, too—the Mexicans."

This was wonderful news to the two chieftains. For well they knew that the Americans had weapons far superior to their own, and that they were brave—not like the cowardly Mexicans.

They willingly supplied the American general with mules for his campaign into Mexico, and even sent some of their own braves to help. Now they welcomed the Americans into their lands, since this was the reason for their coming.

But the Treaty of Guadalupe Hidalgo, which followed the war with Mexico, wrought a great change in their attitude, although it was some time before they recognized what it meant. By the terms of the treaty, Americans assumed responsibility for the protection of their newly acquired Mexican citizens, and also promised to enforce good behavior by the lawless Apaches and to stop their raiding south of the border.

The Americans tried to explain to the Apaches their reasons for prohibiting further depredations into Mexico. But, argued the Apaches, why should the Americans be so foolish as to protect their former enemies. They had made peace? What then? And they said in no uncertain terms that any attempt on the part of the Americans to stop them from killing their age-old enemies was both stupid and foolish.

Very soon thereafter the Apaches renewed their attacks upon the Americans who traveled in their country.

On a day some years after peace had been made between the

Americans and Mexicans, Cochise received word from Mangas that he earnestly desired to have a talk with him. Cochise went at once to the Mimbreño camp. The two chiefs spent several days together. Below them was a camp of American miners. This camp lay in an unprotected place, and the ridge above, from which Cochise and Mangas watched the activity, was heavily wooded and wonderfully suited for ambush. But neither chief could devise a way to draw the miners up there, and even the bullets from their pesh-e-gars could not reach the miners so far below.

These miners, they saw, had a new and terrifying weapon, which fired many shots before it needed to be reloaded. And these shots carried farther than ever.

"Someone in Was-i-tona [Washington] makes great medicine so those pesh-e-gars can shoot so far," Mangas said.

"Why do the White Eyes care so much for yellow iron?" asked Cochise, as always perplexed by that strange phenomenon. "I have heard that much yellow iron has been found far to the west near the shores of the great sea," he continued.

Cochise was, of course, referring to the discovery of gold in California which had brought hoards of Americans across southern Arizona on their way to the gold fields.

"The wagons of the White Eyes stretch from Was-i-tona to the land where the sun goes down," Cochise said. "Let us look to Holos, my brother, and pray to Usen that no yellow iron is hiding in the mountains of either the Mimbreños or the Chiricahuas in sufficient abundance to bring more White Eyes among us."

The two chiefs sat silently together, contemplating the disaster that threatened their lands.

Chapter 9

Friend of the "White Eyes"

AND STILL THE AMERICANS CAME. ON AND ON ACROSS THE sun-baked country their wagons plodded. Some merely passed through on their way to California. But many remained. Not just the rock scratchers, but men with large wagons in which they brought their women and children and their household goods, their cattle following after. It was these men who caused the People of the Woods the most concern, for they had come to stay.

They built homes and put up corrals for their stock. They fenced off the waterholes, and their noisy guns frightened away the game.

Along the road they traveled were many graves, marked with crudely lettered signs which bore the words KILLED BY APACHES, and the name of the victim and the date of his death. But even these mute reminders of the fate that they might meet did not halt the tide of Americans.

Like all the tribal leaders, both Cochise and Mangas Coloradas were deeply troubled.

One day in the year 1851 Mangas saw a party of Americans bearing strange instruments and engaged in some queer activity near the Santa Rita Copper Mines. As these mines lay right in the heart of his homeland, Mangas spied upon them. And after several days he went to investigate.

The party, which consisted of several scientists and surveyors, had an escort of well-armed soldiers. John Bartlette, the leader, explained to Mangas, through an interpreter, that they were marking the boundary line between the United States and Mexico.

"At the end of the war between our two countries," Bartlette said, "it was not settled which land belonged to Mexico and which to us. So the American government has paid to the government of Mexico ten million dollars for this strip of land we call the 'Gadsden Purchase.'" Ten million dollars, he went on to explain to the baffled Apache, was a large amount of gold.

"But this is our land," Mangas protested. "It has always belonged to us. How could the Mexicans sell it, as it never was theirs?"

"Nantan" (Chief) Bartlette, as the Apaches called him, could make no satisfactory explanation.

When word of this perplexing situation reached the ears of Cochise, he was, at first, highly indignant. He talked it over with Naretena, upon whose counsel he often depended.

"All the country below the Gila River is now American, they

say," he told his brother. "They have 'bought' it from the Mexicans with their yellow iron. This land that has belonged to the Chiricahuas for many, many harvests, now belongs to the White Eyes! They did not remember that it is *our* land—that it has belonged to our people since before the memory of our oldest braves. These mountains, these rocks, these waterholes are ours. The animals that roam this land were put here by Usen to give food to the People of the Woods. How, then, can the Americans take it from us by paying the Mexicans yellow iron?"

Naretena made no answer as he pondered this grave problem. When he did not reply, Cochise said proudly, "We have never been conquered. No warriors on earth have ever defeated us."

At last Naretena spoke. "That is true, my brother," he said. "Yet every moon our people grow less. But the White Eyes are without number. They are like the sands of the desert. Even if we should kill them by the hundreds, there are still more of them who come from the lands in the East. And every harvest they bring more powerful weapons. Soon they will conquer us, unless—"

"Unless what?" asked Cochise harshly.

"Unless we become as they are. Study their ways. Learn from them. In their love of yellow and white iron they are foolish, we think. Yet in most ways they are wise. They are brave, too. They are too strong for us. We cannot destroy them. Unless we learn to walk the road of the White Eyes, the People of the Woods will perish in time."

These were hard words for Cochise to hear, yet he knew his brother spoke the truth. For some time he pondered these words in silence. At last he said, "We will send for Mangas Coloradas and tell him our new plan. I will tell my braves, too, that hereafter we will walk the white man's road and cease molesting them."

"Some of our braves may refuse," Naretena pointed out.

"I am their chief," Cochise said, his dark eyes flashing. "Those who will not join with me must leave our camp. No longer will they belong with the Men of the Rising Sun."

It did not occur to either brother that their tribesmen might refuse in sufficient numbers so that Cochise would be deposed and a new leader elected. For both knew how great and almost mystical was Cochise's hold over his people.

Signal fires were lighted on the mountaintops, inviting Mangas Coloradas and his braves to come for a "big talk." The Chiricahuas provided a great feast for the Mimbreños.

When the feasting was over, Cochise spoke. He related the long history of the enmity between the Mexicans and the Apaches. "The Mexicans say that this land all around us belonged to them," Cochise said. "And now they have sold it to the White Eyes for yellow iron. But remember, my brothers, and meditate on this. This land has not always belonged to the People of the Woods. Long ago other peoples lived on our lands—the Ancient Ones. But now they are here no more. Where have they gone? Why did they go? Because they would not change their ways. Because they went on living in the old way, while all about them things were changing. Let us not be so foolish as they, my brothers," he said earnestly.

Then he went on, "Now the White Eyes have come. They kill Apaches. They hunt us as though we were lobo wolves. They give us no peace. But they are brave, their weapons are powerful. And there is no end to them. With every moon more White Eyes come to our lands. We must learn to walk their road or, before many harvests, we, too, will disappear like the Ancient Ones—and there will be no more Apaches living on the lands of our fathers." A long silence followed Cochise's words. Then he said, "I have spoken."

"My brother speaks wisely," Mangas Coloradas answered at last. "But I know the White Eyes better than he. A few speak the truth, but most speak with a forked tongue. Does my brother really expect us to obey the laws of these people who rob us of the lands of our fathers? Does he expect us to be at peace with Mexicans who still take money for Apache scalps?"

"I am not trying to explain why the White Eyes act as they do," Cochise replied with great dignity. "No man despises Mexicans more than I. I am not thinking of Mexicans. It is the People of the Woods of whom I think—and of their children and their children's children. The White Eyes are here in our lands, and more and more come all the time. They grow stronger, while day by day our people grow weaker.

"The White Eyes have better weapons than we have. And when we take their weapons they bring more and even better ones. When we go hungry they have food. When we are cold they have warm homes to live in. The White Eyes know about things of which our people are ignorant. It would be well for the People of the Woods to learn from the White Eyes."

Again Cochise ceased speaking. Then Mangas Coloradas played his strongest card. Well he knew how deep in the heart of Cochise was his love of truth. Two things, above all, the chief of the Chiricahuas valued—one was bravery, the other truth.

"The White Eyes will not believe my brother when he tells them he wants peace with them," Mangas said slyly.

"Never have I spoken with a forked tongue," Cochise said proudly.

Then, one by one, the braves of the Mimbreños and of Cochise's own tribe spoke their minds.

A certain young Chiricahuan, named Gokliya, who was gaining a reputation among his tribesmen for ruthlessness and cruelty on the warpath, asked, "Does the great chief of the Chiricahuas expect us to live like squaws—to grow things in the earth and become the grandmothers to cattle? Would not our people grow weak and soft if we lived as the White Eyes do?"

"The White Eyes are not weak, nor are they squaws." Cochise spoke firmly. There was silence while the braves replenished the failing fire.

Then Cochise spoke again. "When I make peace with the White Eyes," he said, "it means that the whole land of the Men of the Rising Sun is a place of peace. Whoever refuses to abide by that peace is my enemy. Even you, my brother," he said, turning toward Mangas Coloradas. "I do not want to be an enemy of the great chief of the Mimbreños, but I have never spoken to you with a forked tongue, nor will I do so now. And so I say that if any of your people breaks this peace which I am going to make with the White Eyes, that man becomes my enemy. And to my own people I say," he went on, turning and looking earnestly at the braves of his tribe, "if anyone does not wish to follow me—to learn to walk the white man's road, let him go now. And whenever he is found upon our lands, he will be killed."

A gasp of surprise swept over the assembly. Then Gokliya got to his feet. "I walk away," he said. He was joined by a few of the other Chiricahua braves, but most of them remained seated, indicating that they would follow their chief, no matter where he led.

The Chiricahuas, who had chosen to leave, went to their wickiups for their weapons, their wives and children, then departed from the lands of their fathers.

At last Mangas Coloradas spoke, "The Mimbreños will not

join with the Chiricahuas," he said, "but we will not ride against our brothers." Then Mangas and his braves left, too.

Cochise and Naretena watched the dissenting braves of their own tribe ride away with deep regret. But Cochise would do nothing to stay their departure.

Gokliya came to be known by another name—a name given him by the Mexicans—a name that became synonymous in the annals of the West with treachery and deceit—a name that was to spread terror all over the territory. *Geronimo!*

In the days and months that followed, Cochise was often to find that Mangas had spoken truly when he said that the Americans would not believe in Cochise's sincerity. To most of the Americans who entered and settled in Apacheria, the "only good Indian was a dead Indian." Cochise found it difficult to find an American Nantan (chief) with whom to deal, but he persevered. He welcomed every opportunity to prove his friendship to the Americans.

On the high slopes of the Chiricahua Mountains, the members of Cochise's band made a permanent camp, near a place that came to be called Apache Pass. Here Cochise had been born, and here his father Nachi had lived for many years. Here were located more Strongholds of the Chiricahuas—rugged sanctuaries where the braves rested between battles. Their scouts could see for miles around and have plenty of time to warn of danger. Here a handful of braves could hold off their enemies, and the women and children could stay in safety. Cochise, firmly believing in his new policy, hoped that never again would the Strongholds be needed for defense.

Many of the young braves of his tribe became discontented with these new ways. Their lives had been devoted to raiding and warfare, and they were bored with inactivity. Cochise tried hard to keep them occupied. He organized hoop and pole games, horse racing and wrestling matches, and he sent them off on hunting expeditions toward the north—because Mexico lay to the south, and, although the Chiricahuas still went on an occasional raid into the lands of their old enemies, Cochise believed that someday, perhaps, there would be peace even with them.

"Now we can go on raids into Mexico, even though it is against the laws of the White Eyes," Cochise said to Pionsenay, who had brought him word of the discontent of some of his tribe. "At present they are not powerful enough to stop us. But this will not always be so. When there are enough White Eyes in our lands they can force us to obey all their laws. So let us train our young braves to get used to hunting in the north."

Although the young braves disliked the new ways, the squaws were happy. They became more industrious than ever. They even built their wickiups with more care, knowing that now they could live in them longer.

Some of them, among whom was Nalikadeya, Cochise's second wife, built quite elaborate structures.

Some time before, Cochise had taken Nalikadeya, a handsome young woman of his tribe, for his second wife. By her he had a son—Nachise. Many years before, the first-born child of Tesalbestinay and Cochise had been slain by a Mexican—one of a band of scalp collectors who had stolen into a small camp of the Chiricahuas while the braves were away. He was preparing to remove the little boy's scalp when Cochise came upon him. His fury upset his aim, and the Mexican escaped—but Cochise never forgot his face and vowed torture and death to the Mexican should he ever find him again.

At the time when Cochise sought to make peace with the Americans, his second son, by Tesalbestinay—Tahzay—was about eight years old.

On one of their rare raids into Sonora, the Chiricahuas brought back a herd of fine fat cattle. Most of the braves were disgusted when Cochise said they must raise cattle "as the White Eyes do." They had assumed, of course, that they were getting a supply of beef for immediate use and to be made into jerky. For the first time there was almost open revolt in the tribe. Yet, even in this emergency, Cochise managed to exercise his hold over his people, and they obeyed him, though grudgingly.

The cattle grew fatter than ever on the rich grama grass in the near-by meadows, and the stream near the Stronghold kept them well watered. Soon, to their own astonishment, the tribesmen began taking pride in their herd. Even the most skeptical of the malcontents came to believe that Cochise's ways were good, after all.

One day Cochise's scouts brought him word that a party of Americans were putting up a large, square building near the spring in Apache Pass. Cochise watched the men for a day or two, wondering what was afoot.

"Why not go and find out?" Naretena asked. "This is your chance to make friends with some White Eyes."

"Come with me," Cochise said. "Let us take Pionsenay, Skinyea, Nahilzay and Juan with us." So Naretena went to summon the braves whom Cochise had mentioned.

In a short time they appeared at Cochise's wickiup in full war regalia; their faces painted a bright vermilion, each brave armed with a lance and bows and with quivers of arrows on their backs.

Cochise was furious. "Take that paint off your faces," he stormed. "And leave your weapons in your wickiups. We do not go to make war on these White Eyes! We go in peace!"

The braves started to protest, but Cochise silenced them

with a gesture. Soon they returned, their faces innocent of war paint. Except for a hunting knife which every Apache always carried in the fold of his long moccasins, they were completely unarmed. Mounting their ponies, they rode swiftly down to the springs, near which the Americans were working.

"Apaches!" cried one of the white men. It was almost a scream of terror. They hid behind the partly built wall of the structure. Each man seized his rifle.

Cochise rode up to the one man who was not terrified at their approach.

"Howdy, my brother," he said, smiling. "I am Cochise, chief of the Chiricahua Apaches and friend of the Americans. What are you doing here?"

The man, whose name was Wallace, explained that they were building a stage station—one of many being erected along the long route reaching from El Paso, in the East, to San Francisco in the West. Wallace spoke in Spanish as Cochise had.

"Stagecoaches will come through this pass, carrying travelers from the East to their destinations in the West," he explained.

"I live in the mountains up there," Cochise said, "with my warriors and their squaws and children. My people are at peace with the Americans. But there are some bad Apaches who roam this land. Especially one now called Geronimo. He and his band kill Americans and steal their mules and cattle. You must be careful of them. My scouts will watch for them and we will protect you if we know that they are planning an attack."

In spite of the unsavory reputation of Apaches, Wallace was discerning enough to know that this one was speaking the truth.

"Come out here, you lily-livered fools," he called in English to the others who were still cravenly hiding behind the adobe wall. "Come and meet a friend."

Fearfully, one by one, the others crept from their hiding place. Cochise saluted them in friendly fashion, as though unaware of the fear which he and his braves had provoked.

And so began the friendship between the men at the stage station and Cochise's Chiricahuas.

When the work was completed, Wallace and two others, Culver and Walsh, stayed behind to take charge of the station. Their job was to supply fresh horses to the many stages; to see that the passengers were fed and had a place to rest after riding the rough and weary miles; and to do other work necessary for the station's maintenance. A small building had been built near the station for the soldiers believed to be needed in this land of the "bloodthirsty savages." But for some time Fort Bowie, as this station was named, had no need of soldiers. For Cochise was as good as his word. He did, indeed, "protect" the station as he had promised to do, as well as the stagecoach passengers themselves.

Several times, during the first months the stages were operating, other Indians did attempt to raid them. But through smoke signals the Chiricahuas were warned by their scouts of the intended attacks, and always the braves of Cochise's band arrived in time to scare off the raiders.

One time, however, shortly after the blast of the stagecoach horn sounded in the hills signaling its approach, five Apaches in full war garb, lances in hand and armed with bows and arrows, began circling around the oncoming coach. As they came within shooting range each Indian disappeared behind the body of his horse, one hand grasping its withers—just one foot showing above the animal's back. Occasionally a painted face appeared for a moment under the horse's neck, then instantly vanished. The attackers galloped in a circle around the coach, while flight after flight of arrows whistled past it.

The passengers were too terrified to aim their rifles accurately. Both the driver and the guard, seated on the box, fired at the raiders with no success, except that they killed one horse.

Soon both the driver and the guard were wounded and unable to shoot.

Suddenly more Indians galloped full tilt down the mountainside and began attacking the first Indians. And then the American passengers witnessed a terrifying sight. The defending Indians lassoed the attackers. They took their arms away from them, tied ropes around their bodies and led them before the chief of the rescuers, Cochise himself.

Cochise recognized two of the men as former members of his own band who had "walked away." The other three were strangers to him. They were men from other tribes who had allied themselves with the former Chiricahuan—Geronimo.

In hoarse, guttural tones, Cochise pronounced sentence upon them. They had disobeyed his order—had trespassed on his lands—and now they must die.

The captives watched in silence while Cochise's braves drove five stout poles into the hard earth. They said not a word as they were bound to these poles with ropes of rawhide. Nor did they speak when the Chiricahuas started fires at their feet. Even when the flames enveloped them, they uttered no word of protest. With Indian stoicism they accepted their fate.

When the five captives were dead, their bodies were removed from the poles and placed together in one large grave.

Then Cochise saw the stagecoach safely on its way and later returned to his Stronghold.

The men left on guard at the station never mentioned this affair to Cochise and his braves, but they expressed their gratitude in more tangible ways. Presents of food, blankets, trinkets, even firearms were given the Chiricahuas.

Cochise and his tribesmen entered into a never-before-known relationship with these white men—they began working for them for pay. They hauled wood from the mountains and chopped it into stove-length pieces. They cut grama grass from the meadows and carried it to the corrals. They even roamed the land to procure rare herds of wild horses, which they lassoed and then broke to haul the stagecoaches of the white men.

With some of the money they earned the Chiricahuas often bought things from the small store at the station, run by a white man named Tevis.

This friendly relationship was not all based either on the work the Chiricahuas did or the protection they afforded. For the white men enjoyed inviting their Apache friends to feasts at the station. Sometimes they even played together.

The Chiricahuas loved to ride in the coaches between Apache Pass and Dragoon Springs. Agent Wallace, who became their special friend, allowed as many Chiricahuas to go for a ride as could crowd into the vehicles. They helped hold the spirited steeds quiet while they were harnessed and hitched to the traces of the coach. Then the driver on the box, reins in hand, gave the command, "Let go of all," and off the horses dashed at breakneck speed through the canyons, over the mountains and across the plains—the Apaches yelling with glee and taking turns blowing mighty blasts on the horn.

But the good feeling between the white men and their red brothers exhibited at the Overland Stage Station at Apache Pass was not general throughout the territory. Every week word was brought to Cochise of the troubles the red men were suffering at the hands of the whites. Messages came from Mangas Coloradas telling of the killing of his Mimbreños. From the Pinals, the Tontos and the Mescaleros came the same report. Apaches were being hunted like wild animals and killed whenever found—or if they were not killed they were "put behind fences" which was Cochise's way of describing reservations.

To Cochise, a reservation was worse than death. "It is better to kill an eagle than put it in a cage," he told Naretena.

The chieftains of the other tribes urged Cochise to join with them in driving the white invaders from their lands. For once all the Apaches, who had so often warred with one another, were united against this common enemy.

Cochise knew that once safe in their impregnable Stronghold his people could not be found. But Apaches of other tribes were not so fortunately located. In thinking of the Chiricahuas, was he lacking in loyalty to all Apaches?

His wise younger brother spoke the words that gave him courage to pursue the path he had chosen. "There is only one way to save the People of the Woods," Naretena said, "and that is to prove to the White Eyes that they and we can live together as brothers. No matter what others may think, there is no disloyalty in the heart of a leader who works toward that end, my brother."

Although comforted by Naretena's words, Cochise was deeply troubled and sorely perplexed.

Chapter 10

Betrayal

FROM HIS PERCH HIGH IN THE MOUNTAINS ABOVE APACHE Pass, Cochise looked out over the hills and valleys.

"Soldiers," he remarked to Naretena. "For many moons no soldiers have come here. What does it mean, I wonder?"

"Let us go down to the station," his brother suggested. "Our good friend Nantan Wallace is there. He will tell us."

"Let me go with you, my husband," Nalikadeya spoke up. "I want to buy at the white man's store. Let us take Nachise with us. He loves to see the pretty things at the store of Nantan Tevis."

Cochise laughed. "You always want something from the

store of Nantan Tevis," he remarked indulgently. "Enju, you may both come with us. We will take Tali and Wa-ka-dah with us, also. Perhaps our American friends may be needing more wood."

The day was very hot. Cochise, Naretena, Tali and Wa-ka-dah, the two grown sons of Juan, wore only breechclouts and moccasins. Nalikadeya wore a light cotton shirt and a skirt. Little Nachise was naked except for his tiny moccasins. As they journeyed down to the station they saw that the soldiers had left and had made camp a short distance away.

Soon Cochise and his party arrived at the station. Culver came out to greet them. Cochise sat down and started to talk. "Soldiers were here," he said.

"They are from Fort Buchanan," Culver replied.

"They are on their way to the Rio Grande," Wallace added. "The officer who leads them said he was going to make a camp near here. He said that if I saw you to tell you he would like you to make him a visit." A wave of suspicion swept over Cochise, but it was quickly dispelled by Wallace's next words. "He's new here. He has just recently joined the soldiers at Fort Buchanan. He said that there is a white flag flying over his tent."

"We will go and visit with the soldiers," Cochise said. Then, as he rose to go, he asked, "Do you need more wood?"

"Yes," Culver answered.

"Enju," said Cochise. "We will get it after we have seen the new soldier nantan."

Confidently the Chiricahuas approached the camp of the soldiers. There was no suspicion in Cochise's mind, for many harvests had passed since he had had any trouble with white men. This would be just an ordinary visit with presents given and vows of friendship exchanged.

Cochise and the others walked straight to the tent over which the white flag of truce flew in the breeze. Outside the tent there was a large man with a heavy black beard—a veteran Indian fighter named Bernard. Three other men were inside. One was a smooth-faced young fellow with a sun-burned countenance, who seemed to be in command. Cochise dismissed him as being too young to bother about. But he did not like the looks of a heavy-set older man with small, crafty eyes. The third was a Mexican, whom the others called Antonio.

As soon as Cochise and his party were seated, the crafty-faced man got up and went outside. Cochise heard the sound of the heavy boots of soldiers after the man, whose name he learned was Ward, left the tent.

Ward returned shortly. Cochise saw him nod to the youth whom he addressed as Lieutenant Bascom. This was one of the strangest things about the white men, Cochise thought. They put young men, scarcely more than babies, in charge of men old enough to be their fathers.

Then Bascom spoke, and the Mexican, Antonio, interpreted his words.

"Cochise," Bascom began abruptly. The Chiricahua chief looked up in surprise as he recognized his name. The young boy-soldier did not know the Apache ways, he thought. He did not know that a man's name was spoken only by those close to him, or at a time of great danger. "I have come for the little son of this man, John Ward, and the oxen and horses your warriors stole from his ranch on the Sonita."

Antonio translated the words. When Cochise understood them his eyes blazed. But he controlled himself immediately. This is only a boy, he thought. He knows no better. He sat in silence for a few minutes. Then he spoke.

"For many harvests the Chiricahuas have been friends with

Americans," he said. "All that time no one of my tribe has stolen anything from the white men—neither child nor animal. If you will describe this child to me, and tell me, too, about the animals that were stolen, I will send some of my braves to other tribes who live near the ranch on the Sonita, and they will try to find them."

"Mr. Ward says it was your warriors who stole them," Bascom replied.

Cochise settled himself comfortably on the ground. This would take some time, he thought, for this youth was not a reasonable person. He was too young and had had no experience in dealing with men. In time, Cochise was sure, he could be made to realize his mistake. Then he would withdraw his accusations and apologize.

"For five harvests my people have not been at war with the white men," he repeated.

Then Naretena spoke up. "My brother speaks true," he said. "It was not our tribesmen who stole the child and the animals. We have been at peace with your people for many harvests."

"Many times I have helped Americans," Cochise went on. "I will do so now. Not far away are the camps of other Apache tribes—the Pinals, the Tontos, the Mescaleros and the Coyoteros. If we find the child in any of their camps we will bring him back."

Ward said something quickly to Bascom, which he did not let the Mexican translate. Cochise did not understand the words, but he knew from the manner in which they were spoken that they were hostile to him.

One after another the Chiricahuas spoke—first Naretena, then each of the sons of Juan. Cochise could see that Bascom did not believe them. It was hard for him to credit what was happening— it had been so long since he had had any trouble with Americans.

For a long time he and his comrades talked. He watched the boy-soldier and saw disbelief and boredom on his face. And in the eyes of Ward there was raw hatred.

Cochise froze. This was really happening—this thing of which Mangas Coloradas had so often warned—the treachery and deceit of Americans. Since the days of Juan José, Americans had lured the red men to their doom under flags of truce. The more Cochise talked, the greater the intolerance of the young soldier became.

There is nothing in his mind which makes for fair dealing, Cochise said to himself. But I have nothing to fear, for I have kept my pledge of friendship to Americans. I know nothing of the boy and the cattle stolen from the ranch on the Sonita River.

As Cochise talked on and on, protesting his ignorance of the theft of child and animals, he saw that his words were having no effect. This realization made him numb, and he knew that the other Chiricahuas shared his apprehension. All the stories he had heard from other tribes passed through his mind. He had frowned upon his people when they had repeated those stories to him.

Yet, in spite of his growing sense of the uselessness of his words, he went on talking, until at last the boy-soldier came to the end of his patience. This was the first time he had ever been in command of a body of soldiers and he must make a showing.

"Cochise," he said abruptly, "you are a damned liar!"

Antonio translated his words. Blood pounded in the veins of the Chiricahua chief. His heart beat violently. He could scarcely breathe.

"You and your people will stay here under guard until the Ward child is brought back," the young lieutenant continued. "Sergeant," his voice was like the cracking of a whip. "Arrest these Apaches. Have one of our army tents set up and put the prisoners inside. Maybe by morning the old liar will tell the truth."

Sergeant Bernard started to protest. It was plain to see that he was not in accord with his commander's attitude. But, although older than the lieutenant both in years and in service, he was obliged to obey him. Bernard summoned the soldiers, who seized the Apaches. They confiscated the hunting knives stuck through the bands of their breechclouts. As soon as the prison tent was ready the Apaches were put inside. Two sentries walked guard before the tent while the other soldiers made camp for the night.

For two hours the prisoners sat in silence, brooding on the injustice of the white man. Finally Cochise spoke—in a low tone filled with emotion. He must somehow prevent a real breach between his people and the Americans, he told them.

"This soldier-captain is only a boy. He should not be in charge as a chief. He does not think. He will shoot us if we do not say that we stole the boy and the cattle. But we did not steal them— and we know nothing of them. There is only one thing to do. When darkness comes we will escape."

"But the soldiers are at the tent door," said Tali. "They are armed and we are not. They even took away our knives. The door of the tent is tied. Before one of us could get out they would shoot us all."

Cochise smiled. He reached inside his breechclout and drew out his hunting knife from the place where he had hidden it when the soldiers first approached.

"I will cut a hole in the back of the tent," Cochise said. "We will all leave through it. We must make no noise. If they catch one of us, the others must run to our camp for help. Then the boy-soldier will listen to reason, maybe."

When night came Cochise carefully slit the tent at the back

and crawled out. Two soldiers saw him and fired their rifles. But Cochise had seen them, too, and as they took aim he rushed away. A bullet struck him in the leg, but the other shots failed to hit him. He ran, leaving a trail of blood on the ground. A short distance away he tore off his breechclout, bound it quickly around his wounded leg, and escaped to the mountains.

An alarm sounded and the soldiers rushed to the back of the tent. They saw the other Apaches attempting to escape. Tali was struck in the belly by the bayonet of the same soldier who had shot Cochise.

The soldiers seized all the male Apaches and bound them hand and foot. Bascom ordered ten of his men to go in pursuit of Cochise. They pretended to obey, but they knew too much of the ways of Apaches to do more than pretend. For half an hour they hid behind rocks near the camp, then returned and reported that Cochise could not be found.

By a secret path Cochise went toward his Stronghold, about forty miles away. On the way he met twelve of his braves, led by Pionsenay and Skinyea, who had worried because Cochise and the others had not returned and had come to find out what was delaying them. Cochise quickly told them what had happened. Then he dispatched two braves to the Stronghold for reinforcements.

"Two American rock scratchers are camping in a dry wash near Apache Pass," Cochise told Skinyea. "Go and capture them. In the morning, when Holos first looks over the mountains, bring them to the ridge above the stage station. Do not kill them. I want those White Eyes alive so I can trade them for our people the boy-soldier is holding in his tent."

Ever on the watch, the wily chief placed a number of his braves in the canyon through which the horses must pass in order to reach the springs. As the men drove the horses before them, the Chiricahuas fell upon them, stampeding the animals and wounding two of the soldiers.

The following day Cochise appeared on the ridge above the stage station. With their chief were a hundred warriors—their faces smeared with paint. Eagle feathers jutted from their headbands. They were all heavily armed with lances, rifles, bows and arrows. Some distance ahead of his braves, in full ceremonial regalia, rode Cochise. His face, too, was covered with black and red and yellow paint. With him were the two American prospectors whom Pionsenay and Skinyea had captured.

Cochise came well within shouting distance of the camp, but out of gunfire range.

"Agent Wallace," he shouted, "tell the boy-soldier I have two American prisoners to trade for my three Chiricahuas."

Wallace told the young lieutenant what Cochise had said. But the intolerant boy-soldier paid no heed. He refused Cochise's offer, threatening to hang the three male Apaches if the Americans were not immediately released and the horses returned.

Then Cochise hurled defiance at the young soldier. "I will kill these Americans unless my Chiricahuas are not released at once," he cried.

"For heaven's sake," shouted one of the prisoners, "make the exchange, Lieutenant. These Indians are on the warpath. Do not sacrifice our lives."

But the arrogant young soldier turned a deaf ear to the plea.

"Lieutenant," urged Sergeant Bernard, "make the trade as Cochise asks. You were wrong to arrest him in the first place. If you aren't careful you will revive the old Apache war."

"Mind your own business," snapped Bascom. "You will be court-martialed for this insubordination."

Meanwhile Wallace, who understood the Apache nature and saw the injustice of the situation, sensed the danger.

"I am an old friend of Cochise's," he told Bascom. "I will go over and talk to him." Then Wallace approached Cochise and his braves.

For the first time in the years of their friendship there was no smile of greeting on the face of the Chiricahua chief as he saw Wallace. It was this man, Cochise remembered, who had told him the white nantan wanted to see him. He had said the flag of truce was flying over the soldier's tent.

Cochise spoke sharply. "What have you to say to me?" he asked.

"I have come to ask you to release your prisoners first," Wallace replied. "Then, I am sure, the lieutenant will set your Chiricahuas free. Do this, Cochise," Wallace begged. "That is the only way to prevent war."

"The boy-soldier was the first to take prisoners," Cochise replied in icy tones. "He must be the first to let them go."

"That would be fair if we were dealing with a grown man," Wallace answered. "But this boy is not a man. He has had no experience. He is fresh out of a school for soldiers, and he wants to show his authority. For the sake of your people, do as he says. All will be made right in two days more, when the older soldiers from Fort Buchanan arrive. I give you my word that I am speaking the truth."

But Cochise would not trust this White Eye now, remembering that it was Wallace who had sent him into the trap.

"Go with my decision," Cochise answered.

At this moment one of the prisoners broke away from his captors and rushed toward the fort. A brave of Cochise's tribe sent shots after him. When close to the fort he was killed.

But he had not been killed by the shots of the Chiricahuan. The eyes of the men at the fort were blinded by fear. They believed that the Apaches had started an attack. They thought the escaped prisoner was an Apache brave.

"They have all eaten of the lieutenant's locoweed," Wallace cried. Then the white soldiers began to shout. Cochise told his braves to be quiet so that Wallace could hear what they were saying and interpret their words. As he listened, Wallace's face grew pale. He felt the Angel of Death very near him.

The other prisoner also heard the words the soldiers shouted. He, too, was thoroughly frightened, and he cried loudly, "No! No! No!"

Wallace turned toward Cochise. "The madman says he will hang your three braves unless you release this man and return the horses at once."

"He will not dare do that," said Cochise.

"Yes, Cochise, he will," Wallace said. "The young madman thinks it his duty to teach you Apaches a lesson. Do as he says. If you fail us, none of us will have a chance."

"Tell him that we will kill our prisoner and many other White Eyes if he does not release my Chiricahuas at once," answered Cochise.

"Would you kill me, Cochise?" asked Wallace.

For answer Cochise ordered his braves to strip off his clothes. Then he held Wallace's naked body so that the Americans could see him and hear his cries. Wallace broke away and started to run in a zigzag direction to the stage station. Pionsenay spurred his horse, swung his reata and veered back toward Cochise at full gallop, dragging the body of Wallace behind his horse.

Cochise ordered Pionsenay to stop, but the other Chiricahuas were yelling defiance at the white soldiers and the chief's words could not be heard.

When Pionsenay's horse finally stopped, Wallace was dead—

his body crushed and bruised from the rocks over which he had been dragged.

Meanwhile the message sent by Lieutenant Bascom had reached Fort Buchanan. Some soldiers, under Lieutenant Moore, hurried to the stage station at Apache Pass. Moore realized that young Bascom must have handled the whole affair very badly. He came in a conciliatory frame of mind, hoping to pour oil on troubled waters. On the way, he and his men had a brush with a band of Coyoteros returning from a raid. Three of the Coyoteros were captured by Lieutenant Moore's men, and were taken with them to the stage station.

Before reaching Apache Pass, Moore made a detour to Cochise's rancheria in the Chiricahua Mountains. Near the camp they came upon the dead bodies of Wallace and the other prospector captured by Pionsenay.

When he saw them, Moore forgot all about his desire to patch up the trouble between young Bascom and Cochise. His only thought was to avenge this savagery. When he reached the stage station he ordered Bascom to hang the three captured Coyoteros along with his Chiricahua prisoners.

And so Bascom—the boy-soldier—ordered the Chiricahuas taken from the tent. When they saw the look on the faces of the Americans they realized what was in store for them. Naretena and Wa-ka-dah, the unwounded son of Juan, held Tali, the other son—whose bayonet wound had not been treated— upright between them.

Naretena touched the head of Nachise, Cochise's little son, in parting. Then he turned to Nalikadeya and spoke softly. "Tell him this is the work of only one American—one too young to know better," he said. "Tell him not to let it take him from his path."

The soldiers took the three Chiricahuas and the three Coyoteros to a mound in the midst of a grove of oak trees. They selected the largest of the trees, and upon it, the Indians were hanged.

Nalikadeya and Nachise were taken to Fort Buchanan in a wagon. There they stayed for several days and were finally let go.

On the afternoon of the day the Indians were hanged, a violent storm arose. The wind blew furiously. Lightning streaked the sky, showing the stark peaks in its brilliant flashes and revealed the dead bodies swinging from the branches of the great oak tree.

Cochise took three of his best warriors—Nahilzay, Skinyea and Pionsenay—and together with Juan, the father of two of the victims, cut down the bodies. They buried the three Coyoteros together in one grave near the spot where they were hanged. The Chiricahua dead were placed on the backs of their horsees and carried through the rain and pealing thunder to the west Stronghold.

There they were dressed in their finest garments. Their faces were washed and painted red and yellow. Their sacred tzi-daltais were put upon their bodies. Then they were held upright on their best horses and led to a small canyon.

They were buried in graves with their heads facing west. Their weapons were put in beside them. Dirt was thrown over their graves, then leaves and rocks. Cochise stabbed each of the horses in the throat and let the blood fall upon the graves.

The mother and the wives of Juan's two sons cut their hair, blackened their faces and donned old and ragged clothes. They mourned—and Cochise and Tesalbestinay mourned also.

When Nalikadeya and Nachise returned from Fort Buchanan, having walked all the way, she, too, joined in the mourning.

For many days there was no sound in the camp except the crying of the bereaved women. During those long days of mourning Cochise said no word and none of his tribe spoke to him.

Then, when the time of mourning was finished, Cochise called his warriors together. When they were all assembled, he took from his head his red turban and threw it on the ground. He lifted his face toward the sky. And his voice rang out in rage so terrible that the most hardened of the Apaches shuddered.

"I swear vengeance upon the White Eyes," he said. "We will not stop fighting until ten White Eyes have been killed for every Apache slain. No one will be spared. There will be no end to this war until every White Eye is driven from our land. This I pledge! This I pledge! This I pledge!"

With two medicine sticks Nan-ta-do-tash, the very old medicine man, lifted the red turban from the ground and placed it on the head of Cochise. Once again the chief cried, "There will be ten White Eyes killed for every Apache slain. This I pledge!"

For four nights a war dance was held in the camp of the Chiricahuas. During the last night Cochise sent a messenger to Mangas Coloradas to say that he, the Chiricahua chief, would join with the great leader of the Mimbreños. Then he ordered fires lighted on the tops of the jagged mountains, calling the Apaches of all the tribes to war against the White Eyes.

After the messenger departed and the signal fires were lit, the braves still danced around the fire. But Cochise silently made his way to the grave of his brother and sat beside it, weeping, until Holos once again appeared over the mountains, flooding the land with light.

Chapter 11

The Vow Fulfilled

"TEN WHITE EYES SHALL DIE FOR EVERY APACHE SLAIN,"
Cochise had pledged. Now he set out to make good that
vow.

"I have called you," he said to Mangas Coloradas, the first
to arrive at the Stronghold of all the chiefs whom Cochise had
summoned, "to unite the Chiricahuas with the Mimbreños in
war against the truce killers until we have driven the White
Eyes from our lands forever." Then he told Mangas the story
of the betrayal of the Chiricahuas by the boy-soldier under a
flag of truce.

Mangas Coloradas did not answer in words. For some mo-

119

ments he sat in silence. Then he removed his shirt and turned his back upon the younger chief, whose eyes were fixed on the scarred ridges and welts on his back. "This, too, was done under a white flag, my brother," Mangas said in answer to the unspoken question in Cochise's eyes.

"The rock scratchers were invading my country," he went on. "I thought up a plan to get rid of them. I well knew that there is much yellow iron lying to the north of the lands of my people. So I told these rock scratchers—not all at once, but one at a time—that I could lead them into a place where they could find their yellow iron in great quantities.

"They did not believe that I spoke the truth. As most of them speak with forked tongues, they believe that all men do. Especially do they mistrust Apaches. So some of them seized me as I went on a peaceful mission to their lodges. They stripped me and stood me up against a tree. Then they laid their bull whips on my back, giving me a hundred lashes. I lost my senses under this beating—and when I fell, they kicked me as I lay on the ground at the foot of the tree.

"No one before has looked upon these wounds, my brother, but for every stroke from the whips of the White Eyes, many have fallen."

Mangas stopped speaking. The eyes of Cochise burned with hate as he looked at the scarred back.

"Shee-gee," Cochise said, using the term by which Apaches spoke to their dearest friends. "We have been friends for many harvests and have often taken the warpath together. Now on this biggest war we should be more than friends. We shall be blood brothers."

"Enju," responded Mangas.

Then Cochise called his son Tahzay to bring the gourd cup. He put it on the ground before his father. Nochalo, the medicine man, donned his great hat of eagle feathers, for this was the most solemn of all Apache ceremonies. He lit a small fire and put a knife blade in it. Then, taking the wrists of both Cochise and Mangas, he held them up toward the four cardinal directions. Then he let go of their wrists. He took from the fire the heated knife, then waved it, too, in the four directions, before he plunged it into the earth.

The knife was still hot when he cut the flesh of Cochise's right arm a few inches above the wrist. He held the arm of Cochise over the gourd, letting the blood flow into it. Then he did the same thing to the arm of Mangas Coloradas, letting his blood fall into the cup, too. Then he placed their arms together so that the cuts touched, allowing the blood of both chiefs to mix. For several minutes he held their arms together, then he let them go.

With that, Nochalo said solemnly, "Drink." Cochise stooped and picked the cup from the ground and handed it to Mangas, who took a deep drink of their mingled blood. Cochise did likewise.

When the ceremony was over, Cochise faced Mangas and said, "Shee-kizzen" (my brother).

"Shee-kizzen," said the other braves in chorus, and forever thereafter Cochise and Mangas Coloradas were known throughout all of Apacheria as blood brothers.

The chieftains of many tribes came to the council at the Chiricahua Stronghold, and heard from Cochise's lips of the treachery of the Americans. Cochise even welcomed Geronimo, whom he had banished from the lands of the Chiricahua at the time he had decided to "walk the white man's road." For he had need of the fiercest and most ruthless warriors for this new war, and in this respect Geronimo had no peer.

All the chiefs swore to fight under Cochise in this war

against the White Eyes, and promised a thousand braves among them.

"We must never fight unless we are sure of victory," Cochise said. "If we lose one of our number, even though we kill many enemies, we have gained nothing. Only attack when you are sure of complete success. Never risk a single Apache life unless you must."

Cochise fulfilled his vow a hundredfold. His braves were everywhere—waylaying traders, trappers, ranchers and soldiers. Especially did they attack rock scratchers, for it was men like them who had beaten Mangas Coloradas.

But still the white men came with their traps and their tools, with bigger wagons and more deadly guns. And with their coming, the price the Apaches paid rose ever higher.

One day smoke signals rose from a peak in the east end of Apache Pass. Six long-bearded men, who were forever after known to the Apaches as the "Six Tall Men"—and the time of their coming was called the "Day of the Six Tall Men"—were seen traveling through the pass toward the west. They reached the mouth of the canyon and shadows closed upon them, when the Apaches under both Cochise and Mangas Coloradas fired upon them. The Tall Men seemed to be without fear. They stayed on their horses and looked all around. Then they went forward, while the Apaches followed along the canyon walls.

They had to get to the water, even though it meant coming within range of Apache guns. At last they dismounted and hobbled their horses. They put their packs on the ground, then, unconcernedly, they built a breastwork of rocks behind which they sat and lighted their pipes as they looked around for something at which to shoot.

So rarely did they fire their guns that both Cochise and Mangas believed they had only a small quantity of ammunition.

Finally the two chiefs decided to charge. The firing they met from the guns of the Six Tall Men thinned the ranks of the Apaches alarmingly. Twenty Apaches fell dead and others were wounded. There were two strange things about this charge, the chiefs noticed. There were more dead than wounded, and the wounded soon died.

At daybreak the Apaches made another charge. Again they met with heavy losses. Although during the day the Apaches drew back farther and farther from the eyes of the dwindling company, even so, an occasional shot found its mark.

Three of the Tall Men had been still for so long that the Apaches knew they had been killed, but they had paid ten to one for them. Nothing was worth that, Cochise thought. He knew that the white men were suffering terribly from thirst, and that the sound of the water which they could not reach must be maddening them.

It took two more days before the last man alive crawled on hands and knees toward the water. The Apaches were awed by his bravery. They let him drink deeply before they killed him.

When they examined his dead body they saw that his right arm from shoulder to elbow was black from the recoil of his gun, which he had been using steadily for three full days. Even so, he had much ammunition left. His mouth was black. His tongue protruded from the torture of the thirst he had endured.

"They are brave, these White Eyes," said Cochise, as he bent over the body of the last of the Six Tall Men.

Strange news reached the two chieftains. The Americans were at war—not war with the Mexicans, this time, nor just with the Apaches. But war among themselves. Some wore gray suits. They came from the land east of the Mescaleros. They were at war with others who wore blue coats and came from the North. All over the lands of the Apaches was heard the sound of their marching feet.

The wild game was driven farther and farther away. Throughout the lands of both Cochise and Mangas the women and children were hungry. The Apaches were so busy fighting that they had no time to raid.

And still the Americans came on.

While fighting in the lands of Cochise word came to Mangas that once again the American rock scratchers had invaded his own country. Taking his Mimbreño braves with him, he returned to his own encampment. Never before had he seen rock scratchers in such numbers. They were overrunning his lands to an alarming degree. He would never be able to dislodge them without the help of Cochise.

Mangas sent word to the chief of the Chiricahuas, asking him to come and help him rid his country of those abominable rock scratchers. His messengers brought back word from Cochise that he had troubles of his own—that Americans were on their way to his Stronghold from the west.

"Come and help me first," Cochise sent word to Mangas. "Then I will return with my braves and help you retake the mountains of the Mimbreños."

So Mangas once more journeyed to the country of the Chiricahuas, leading his braves. He found that Cochise had not exaggerated his need. A great party of white men was moving eastward. They were coming to Apache Pass where the Six Tall Men had been killed.

"In all these mountains there will be no place for my people if the White Eyes come this way," Cochise mourned. "Already their scouts are camping at Dragoon Springs, only forty miles away from the water in the Chiricahuas. There is no more water between their camp and Apache Pass. If they can be kept from entering here they will have to take the trail to the north around the mountains and my Stronghold will not be invaded."

That night the soldiers of the White Eyes were marching toward Apache Pass. Cochise and Mangas lined the walls of both sides of the canyon with their braves. Both the Mimbreños and his own tribesmen were surprised when Cochise ordered a breastwork of great stones and rocks built overlooking the pass. He had the braves leave crevices between the rocks in which the guns of the Apaches could rest.

While they were waiting for the Americans to arrive at the pass, Cochise noticed a small band of Americans approaching from the east across the plains. He made up his mind to cut them off.

Cochise pointed them out to Mangas.

"I know those White Eyes," Mangas said. "They are rock scratchers from the mines of the Santa Rita. They are very brave men and are always well armed. We can kill them before they enter the pass."

"No," Cochise replied. "We will never let them get so far. We will kill them before they ever reach the pass."

"How can you do that?" Mangas asked. "You cannot surprise them in the open plain."

"This is my country," Cochise retorted, proudly. "I know every foot of it." He called some of his braves to him. "There is a gully a short distance east of the pass," he said to them. "It is as deep as a man is high and twice as wide. A hundred braves could hide there, and no man could be seen by one on horseback until he is almost at the place. Go there and wait for those rock scratchers who are coming."

Cochise's braves took off all their clothing except their breech-clouts and moccasins. Then they rolled themselves in the dust until their painted bodies looked exactly the color of the earth.

They silently slid down the side of the pass and in a few minutes more could not be seen.

The group of miners came closer and closer. They were so sure that they would not be attacked in such an open place that they rode carelessly. Their rifles rested across their saddles. Their pistols were in their holsters. Could they not see for miles in every direction in the flat treeless country through which they were going?

When they were less than forty yards from the gully, Cochise's braves fired upon them. Half a dozen miners fell dead. The rest, panic stricken, tried to escape, but were killed before they had gone twenty yards. Then the Chiricahua braves came out of their hiding place and stripped the dead miners of their guns and ammunition. They found a pouch of yellow gold dust on one of the miners—some of that yellow iron by which these strange creatures set such store—for which they would run any risk, no matter how great. The Chiricahuas had learned how valuable that yellow iron was—that it could be traded for much ammunition, for many guns and for food. So they took it from the body of the slain miner and carried it back to Cochise.

Now the blue-clad soldiers were getting nearer and nearer the pass. Cochise watched them approaching. They were sure that the soldiers would be killed as easily as the party of miners as soon as they got within gunshot of the Apaches.

"The White Eyes will never reach the water, my brother," Cochise vowed. "They are thirsty, for they have been marching for many hours over the desert with nothing to drink. We will turn them back so that those whom we do not kill will try to make their way northward around the mountains. That will send them into the Mongollons on their eastward way, instead of through your lands. That will be good for both of us. They have two small wagons with them, I see," Cochise went on.

"Maybe there is water in those wagons—maybe they are not as thirsty as I thought."

But Mangas knew that those small wagons did not contain water. For he well remembered that small wagon that had belched death into the camp of Juan José.

"Those wagons are not for water, my brother," Mangas said, and his voice trembled with emotion. "They are fire wagons with rifle tubes and they will mow down our braves like the wind."

But Cochise was not alarmed. "We will see when they are ready and give them nothing at which to fire," he said.

But there was no rest. In the late afternoon the Americans went into the pass. Their horses, as thirsty as the soldiers, smelled the water and rushed ahead. The soldiers' tongues were blackened with thirst from the long, long march over dust and sand.

Before they reached the pass, however, rifle fire sounded from both sides of the canyon. Shots poured down upon the narrow file of soldiers who were strung along the path.

The Americans bent forward. They looked as if they were passing through a hailstorm. Many animals fell, hit by the bullets of the Apaches. But the voice of the white officer rose above the screams of the wounded horses, and the brass voice of the bugle gave the order to advance. The soldiers could see nothing at which to aim. Shots from their guns hit only the rocks behind which the Apaches crouched.

Now the horses with empty saddles and the pack animals climbed up to the springs. The shadows grew deeper. As time went on the Americans were being badly punished, but were unable to do any punishing in return.

Night was falling. Why did they not uncover those fire wagons? Cochise wondered. Then the Apaches heard a strange sound from the brass throat. They responded with wild war whoops, for they believed that they had repulsed the Americans and that they were turning back. For apparently they were making no effort to return the fire of the Apaches. Into the open foothills they bowed under the shots from both flanks. Mangas Coloradas was directing the fire from the south side of the pass, Cochise from the north. Now the last horseman of the soldiers was cut off by the Apaches on Cochise's side. He spurred his mount in the opposite direction and was making a circle through Mangas' braves when his horse was hit by a bullet. Cochise calmly dismounted from his dying horse and chose a mark at which to aim.

Then it was dark. Night had fallen—and to Cochise's surprise, Mangas Coloradas was nowhere to be seen.

In the second day of the battle the Chiricahuas found that they were fighting alone. All of the Mimbreños had gone. Now the Americans did not enter the pass single file as they had the day before. They spread out along the canyon walls, driving all before them.

Cochise remembered Mangas' words about the fire wagons when he had told of the disaster at Juan José's camp years before. "One who has not seen the death-dealing fire wagons cannot know about them," Mangas had said. For the fire wagons opened up and spit out death on the Chiricahuas. The canyons echoed the earsplitting roar of the cannon up and down the cliffs.

This was the first time that Cochise and his braves had ever faced shellfire. Fragments of the missiles scattered in all directions, exploding wherever they struck. This was more than the Chiricahuas could stand. They began retreating over the mountains, leaving the white soldiers in possession of the spring.

Cochise had been too smart when he had ordered the breastworks of rocks built. For the Americans could land the shells from their howitzers among many Indians. The shells hit their targets. After they had found the range, both fieldpieces fired shell after shell upon the panic-stricken Chiricahuas. Their ambush was blasted wide open. The Chiricahuas rose and fled.

Then the canyon was silent. The soldiers, crazed with thirst, rushed to the springs and drank deep of the cool water.

It was the worst defeat the Chiricahuas had ever suffered. Cochise took all the members of his band who were still alive and journeyed to the Stronghold, where he told the squaws and the old men of the great battle at Apache Pass.

"All would have been well," he said, "had they not fired their fire wagons at us. When we have bows and arrows, they have fire sticks," he went on bitterly. "When we have fire sticks, they have powder and ball in one piece. When we take those from them, they bring others that shoot twice as far, then others still that shoot many times without reloading. Then they mount their guns on wagons, and a score of our people fall with the sound that shakes the mountain—"

Cochise's voice rose in a cry of lament. "Where we go to the ends of our borders, they pass through all borders. When we go forth in tens, they come in thousands. When we have made an end of war, they have not begun. Though we make friends with one, another of them destroys that friendship. There is no end of the White Eyes—they are never still. The days of our people are numbered."

Chapter 12

Foe of the White Eyes

IT WAS SOME TIME BEFORE COCHISE LEARNED WHY HE AND his Chiricahuas had had to finish the battle at Apache Pass alone, and what had happened to Mangas Coloradas and his Mimbreño braves.

Just before dark the white soldiers had sent messengers back to their companions. Mangas saw them leave and thought, rightly, that they were going for reinforcements. He decided that if he cut them off and prevented them from reaching their destination, he and Cochise would be able to destroy the white men already in the pass. With fifty of his best mounted warriors he took off after them.

But one of the soldiers had a newly issued breechloader. The steady fire from this hitherto unknown weapon disconcerted the Apaches. Firing their old muzzle-loaders and yelling taunts, they galloped near him, but were afraid to close in upon him.

One shot from the white soldier's gun hit Mangas. At once the other Mimbreños gave up the battle. They lifted their wounded chief from the ground and carried him off across the mountains to the small Mexican village of Janos.

While the Mexican women and children hid in terror behind closed and shuttered windows, they carried the bleeding body of their chief straight to the home of a Mexican doctor.

"You make Indian well," Delgadito, a Mimbreño who acted as spokesman, said to the doctor. "He no die, everybody live. He die, everybody in Janos die, too."

While the terrified doctor removed the bullet from the breast of the Mimbreño chief, the people of the little village kept vigil outside his house. Upon his skill depended not only his life, but the lives of all of them. Never did a doctor operate under greater stress.

Owing largely to the iron constitution of the Apache, he recovered, and next day he rode out of town.

Before long, after his return to his own lands, Mangas came to realize the uselessness of trying to resist the all-powerful white men. He lost interest in Cochise's war and attempted to resume friendly relations with the Americans.

One day he and fourteen of his men were out deer hunting, not far from Fort McLean, where a company of California volunteers was camping. One of the soldiers approached Mangas in a friendly manner and invited him to go for a "peace talk" with his captain. Heedless of the warning looks of his tribesmen, Mangas went off alone with the white man to the camp of their soldiers. Once there, he was seized and made a prisoner.

"The white man's flag of truce is the same color as the Mex-icans," Mangas remarked bitterly.

That night he lay in his blanket, his bare feet stretched toward the fire. Through half-closed eyes he watched one of his guards heating the point of a bayonet in the glowing embers. When the bayonet was red hot the guard signaled a sergeant who was standing in the shadows near by. Then he pressed the hot blade against the bare sole of his captive's foot. Mangas sprang up with a cry of pain. Three shots rang out from the pistol in the hand of the watching sergeant, and the great Mimbreño chieftain lay dead.

Over desert, mountain and valley Delgadito ran, carrying the story to Cochise. The Mimbreños had learned the fate of their chief from the lips of a Mexican, whom they had captured and tortured until he told them of Mangas' betrayal and murder.

"And this, too, was done under a flag of truce?" Cochise asked.

"Yes," the Mimbreño brave answered. Cochise's face became a mask of hatred. The pupils of his eyes were like pieces of rock.

"Death to the White Eyes!" he cried. But even as he spoke, he knew that in time he must lose.

Later, when a delegation from the tribe of the Mimbreño Apaches visited him, asking him to take over the war leadership of their people, he agreed. "I will be your leader," he said, "and hereafter you will be the same to me as my own people. But we cannot win, for the White Eyes are as numerous as grasshoppers and as treacherous as lobo wolves." To the leaders of the other tribes whom he had asked to join him in the war on the white men, Cochise said, "It is better that we die together, for die we will, but we shall not die alone." His eyes were sad and solemn as he spoke those fatal words.

For a time, however, Cochise came to believe that perhaps his people were not doomed, after all. Indeed, there was great rejoicing all over Apacheria when the two army posts in the territory, Fort Buchanan and Fort Breckenridge, were abandoned by the soldiers, and all the supplies that could not easily be removed were destroyed. Knowing little of the struggle between the North and South which had called up all the soldiers in the country, the Apaches believed that they themselves were responsible for the abandonment of the forts. They need only take a firm stand, so they thought, and all would be well. The white soldiers would scurry off like frightened hares.

But at the close of the Civil War the Apaches learned how mistaken they were. For then, the Army of the United States devoted itself to trying to take care of the so-called "Indian Problem," everywhere in America.

Terror reigned, especially in Arizona. For twelve years Cochise and his warriors ravaged a huge area, which stretched from the Gila far into Old Mexico, and east into New Mexico to the Mimbres River. The impregnable Stronghold of Cochise's tribe reached far back among the canyons and peaks of the Dragoon and Chiricahua Mountains. From those hiding places the Chiricahua chief sent out small bands of the best braves from all the tribes which had joined with him, far and wide, to rob wagon trains, stampede and capture the cattle and kill unprotected settlers.

As always, they rarely risked an open attack upon well-armed men. From their lookouts his scouts watched for parties of travelers foolhardy enough to go about in small numbers. In some favorable spot the braves ambushed the party, killing the men and carrying off the women and children.

As time went on, the promise that Cochise had displayed—both as a commander and strategist at the time of his father's death—was realized again and again.

No soldiers ever sent against the Chiricahuas were able to cope with them. Beside the clumsy tactics of the white men the superiority of the Apaches was proved many times. To their minds the white man's habit of holding a hot position was just plain silly. When either advancing or retreating, they were careful never to expose an inch of their bronze hides. But the white soldiers had to expose themselves while trying to reach their foes. Consequently, for every Apache killed by the soldiers, from ten to twenty Americans "bit the dust."

It is not to be wondered at that the warriors of the Chiricahuas kept up their unceasing efforts to "turn live Americans into dead ones," especially after they learned of the "extermination policy" promulgated by General Carleton. This was the order that the American general sent out to all his soldiers: "Apache men are to be slain whenever and wherever found. The women and children may be taken prisoners, and need not necessarily be killed."

The so-called "Pinole Treaty," famous in the annals of the Southwest as the ultimate in American treachery, is an example of how Carleton's order was obeyed. The Pinal Apaches had never taken part in Cochise's war. They had always tried to live in peace with their white brothers. Even when the game upon which they depended for food was driven away, they still refused to take up arms against the Americans.

One day it was reported to Paramuca, chief of the Pinals, that American settlers were building homes and corrals on the land where his squaws had always planted corn in the spring to provide food for their people. Some of his wild young men wanted to make war on these white invaders, but Chief Paramuca said, "Killing Americans will solve nothing, for more will come in their stead. And if we kill them, soldiers with white skins will come, too." He suggested their aligning themselves with the Coyoteros and growing corn on the lands of that tribe. This they did, but there was not corn enough to take care of all those people when Usen once again laid snow blankets on the mountaintops. When Ghost Face came again, the Pinal Apaches ranged their lands, trying in vain to find food for their people. Hunger stalked their wickiups.

At least four young braves went down to the cabins of the white settlers. They did not go to harm them. All they wanted was food. They returned with five ponies and four head of cattle. "If the white men kill our deer and take our cornland, it is right for us to take their ponies and cattle for food," they argued.

Shortly afterward a hunting party of Coyoteros, who had joined the Pinals, reported seeing about thirty Americans coming down the valley of the Gila. With them were Maricopa and Pima Indians. Paramuca was fearful that this meant war, for when Americans were accompanied by members of the Maricopa and Pima tribes—hereditary enemies of the Apaches— they were surely on the warpath.

Paramuca sent a truce flag to the Americans and asked for a peace talk. His messenger met an American who also carried a flag of truce, and he said that they, too, wanted to make peace.

Two days later the trusting Pinal Apaches met with the Americans, who provided them with a feast of pinole. And what was the result of the peace talk? After the feast, as they all sat together having a supposedly friendly conference around the campfire, the Americans and their Maricopa and Pima allies fired upon the Pinals and Coyoteros, and Apache blood flowed over the ground like melting snow.

When Cochise learned of this latest treachery his face was grim. Once again he vowed, "Death to the White Eyes!" He devoted all his mind and talents to making war and still more war. From his retreat high in the Chiricahuas, he watched all approaches to his Stronghold. He gathered his braves together. Signals were sent from mountain crags warning him of approaching soldiers, telling their number and equipment.

He reverted to the customs of his ancestors—the long march, the slaying of the enemy and all the arts of bloody ambush. He revived forms of torture used by his people long ago.

The Mexican government had never suspended their custom of paying a bounty for Apache scalps over the years. Cochise was particularly incensed at this, because it reminded him of the death of his own little son at the hands of the Mexican who was trying to obtain the child's scalp. When his braves once captured a Mexican who was known to have sold Apache scalps to his government, Cochise ordered the cruelest torture of all to be his punishment. But Cochise could not enjoy the screams of the Mexican, nor the sight of him writhing in agony. Just before he died, the Mexican cursed Cochise, who sat by, watching—and that curse and the memory of the Mexican's agony were to haunt the Chiricahua chief the rest of his life.

The Chiricahuas made the stealing of livestock from both white men and Mexicans a regular business. They declared openly that they would have killed off all Mexicans long since, had they not found it profitable to use them for shepherds. They had a joke among themselves: They said the Mexicans were their vaqueros upon whom they depended for their horses and cattle, and the Americans were their teamsters and mechanics who hauled goods for them and supplied them with firearms.

When placers were discovered on the lands of Apacheria, General Carelton provided the miners with all the protection he could. He placed a force of five hundred soldiers on the Gila River, north of the Chiricahua Mountains, to operate from that place. He combined both soldiers and civilians with friendly Indians of the tribes of the Papagos, the Pimas and the Maricopas, together with a few renegade Apaches. As all these people regarded the Chiricahua Apaches with undying hatred, they helped wage unceasing warfare. True, the Indians were given the alternative choice of being put on reservations in the Bosque Redonda, but very few of them ever went there.

One time a band of Chiricahuas took refuge in their own mountains. Hard pressed by the soldiers, they made a dash at night to the west, across the broad valley of Sulphur Springs. Their horses were all but exhausted. While they rode on ahead, three lone braves descended upon the Sulphur Springs ranch house. Inside the strong building a dozen cowboys were sleeping soundly, their six-shooters under their pillows, their rifles loaded and ready near by. A herd of horses was kept behind the walls of a sturdy corral—with the gates locked and barred. The three Apaches took a hatchet from the woodpile, chopped down enough of the corral to open a gap, then rode off with the horses.

It was useless for the white men to give chase. In their usual manner, the Apaches made their escape, and soon the whole band was remounted on fresh horses.

Scarcely a week passed without Cochise and his braves committing deeds of violence and bloodshed. His attacks made from ambush were almost always successful. Sometimes he led a large force of warriors. At other times he attacked with only a handful of followers. When necessary, he made a stand with a force sufficient in size to resist all attempts to take him.

Cochise himself led most of these attacks. No Apache could send an arrow straighter to its mark. And he became just as skillful with firearms of the white man as with the primitive weapons of the Indians. His strong lithe body moved quickly. But apart from his own skill as a fighter, much of his success was due to the unswerving loyalty of his followers and his ability to keep them fed and fighting for weeks in succession.

On one occasion, which reminded Cochise of his first raid as a war novice, a few Chiricahuas raided a ranch near Arivaca which was operated by a wealthy ranchero. Here work mules were kept at night in an adobe corral. The great gate which fastened it was made of a heavy iron chain lashed together with lengths of rawhide.

In a building near by white cowboys slept, their firearms beside them. Not one of them heard the stealthy approach of the Chiricahuas. First they tried to saw through the thick adobe walls with their stout hair ropes, but the walls were too strong for that. So the wily Apaches cut the rawhide bindings and unfastened the chains, wrapping their serapes around the iron bars to deaden the sound as they removed them. The sleeping vaqueros had no knowledge of what was going on until they heard the mules and horses being driven away. Twelve armed men followed the Apaches, but they soon ran into ambushes and were killed.

As their raids on the white men were more and more successful, the boldness of the Apaches increased. They stole horses and cattle right outside the walled town of Tucson, well supplied with soldiers.

One time Tahzay, Cochise's eldest son—together with a few braves—ran off a flock of sheep which were grazing in the foothills less than two miles from the town. This happened in broad daylight. The sheep were being guarded by a young Mexican shepherd, who kept his ears open for the tinkle of the bell on the neck of the bellwether. It was very hot that day.

The Mexican lad grew sleepy. At last he dozed, rousing himself every now and then to listen for the bell. Reassured by hearing its tinkle, he assumed that his sheep were still safely grazing near by.

But when he finally woke up, he saw Tahzay leering at him, as he shook the bell which he had removed from the bellwether fully two hours before. By that time the flock of sheep, of course, was far away.

Apaches did not always kill their victims, even when they had the chance. Once Cochise and a band of thirty braves overtook a white man named Bill Kirkland, who was hauling lumber out of the Santa Rita Mountains. The Indians were hungry, having had no food for two days, and Kirkland was well supplied with provisions. Cochise ordered him to kill an ox and roast it, and to prepare other food for them. No doubt because Kirkland—unlike most Americans and all Mexicans—when face to face with Apaches showed no fear, but went steadily to work preparing a feast for them, Cochise did not kill him, but sent him on his way with his load of lumber. For the chief of the Chiricahuas always admired a brave man.

Yet in spite of the fact that in all the battles the Chiricahuas fought, more white men were killed than Apaches, there were always more white men who came to take the place of those slain. And month by month the number of Apaches grew steadily less. What should he do? Cochise wondered. It was useless to go on. Sooner or later his people would all perish.

Yet he dared not sue for peace with the truce killers. If he went to one of their camps for a peace talk would he not be met—as had Mangas Coloradas, Paramuca and many others—with more treachery? Better to keep on fighting until all his people were killed. At least they would carry more of the White Eyes with them to the spirit world.

He longed to have someone with whom he could discuss these things as he had with Naretena. Since the death of Mangas, Tesalbestinay was his sole confidante. They had felt even closer since the death of Mangas, for, as she said, "We have each lost a brother." But, close though they were, she was, after all, only a woman—and it was man's talk and man's counsel he craved. Skinyea, Pionsenay and Juan were good warriors—brave in battle—but they had no conception of the doubts and fears that haunted him. Tahzay might someday take that place in Cochise's life, but at present he lacked wisdom as well as years.

At times like this Cochise's need for Naretena was almost more than he could bear, and his hatred of the boy-soldier whose disbelief had caused the death of his brother was fanned into fresh flames.

Chapter 13

Brothers

HIGH ON THE SUMMIT OF A RUGGED RIM OF THE WEST
Stronghold, Indian lookouts watched a white man struggle up
toward the rock-rimmed entrance. Inside the fortress Cochise
was encamped.

Pionsenay came to his chief. "Smoke signals coming all day
since dawn," he said.

"What do they say?" asked Cochise.

"They say, 'I come on a peaceful mission to see the great
chief of the Chiricahuas,'" Pionsenay replied. Then he laughed.
"That White Eye must be a fool," he said. "For many harvests
no white man has looked upon you and lived."

"Either a fool or a very brave man," Cochise said. "Enju. Let him come. See that none of my braves molest him."

Cochise watched in silence as the white man made his way through gorges, ravines and canyons. He saw him climbing hills and sliding over great boulders. Sometimes the gullies of the mountains and sharp clefts were in shadow. They were like tortured creatures of a prehistoric time.

It was late afternoon when the white man sent up his final smoke signal. The Chiricahuas watched as he untied a bundle of evergreen branches. Then they saw him build a small fire and place some of the branches on the flames. Then he spread his blanket over the flames and suddenly lifted it, and a great cloud of black smoke rose upward.

"Fool!" Pionsenay spat out the word. "He says over and over that his mission is one of peace. We have been reading that message for many hours."

Soon the white man extinguished the fire and once again mounted his horse. All about him was the sun-baked rocky earth. Behind many of the boulders along his path lurked the braves of the Chiricahuas, their fingers itching on the triggers of their rifles, or clutching tightly the shafts of their arrows. But no one made a move to stop the intruder—for that was Cochise's order.

There was no sound but the ring of his horse's hoofs on the hard earth. As he neared the rancheria where Cochise was waiting, an eagle screamed. It was the familiar omen.

The white man followed a narrow wash, which turned abruptly to the right. And suddenly he was in the camp of the Apaches. They were all around him, eying him with a studied lack of curiosity, although they noted and registered everything about him. Their eyes were as hard and unyielding as the rocks strewn all around. Their blank faces expressionless.

The braves spoke no word as the tall, red-bearded man made

his way to the place where Cochise was seated. The stranger leaped from his horse and handed his rifle, his pistol and his hunting knife to Tesalbestinay who was standing near by.

"Keep these things for me until I leave," he said in perfect Apache.

In silence he sat down before the chief. The squaws stopped their chatter, ceased grinding corn and sewing moccasins. The naked children left their games. The braves gathered closer. Every eye was on the red-bearded man who had dared come to their camp alone. They knew—all of them, even the smallest child—that for seven long years—years of terror and bloodshed—no white man had come close to their leader and lived.

The stranger looked steadily into Cochise's eyes. Their glances mingled. Once again on a far-away crag an eagle screamed. There was no other sound except the sighing of the breeze as it ruffled the leaves of the junipers and oaks in the forest.

The white man sat in silence, long, tense moments, until Cochise gravely nodded his head. Then he spoke. "I am Captain Jeffords," he said. "I have come for a peace talk."

"Enju. It is well." Cochise's deep voice was grave.

"I am in charge of running the mail between Mesilla, Fort Bowie and Tucson," the stranger went on. "In the last few months fourteen of my men have been killed by the Chiricahua Apaches. My own body is covered with scars from the arrows of your braves. I have come to talk with you of these things."

Again there was silence. All about the hostile braves stood watching. Hate was stamped deeply on their faces. But the eyes of the white man never left the face of the chief. It was as though he was unaware of the menacing Apaches.

And now Cochise spoke. His voice was sharp like the crack of a pistol. "Why should I make talk with you, O White Eye," he asked. "Men of your race are my enemies. They have driven the game from our mountains. They have stolen our lands and poisoned our water holes. They have killed our young men. They have tricked us again and again. White men are truce killers. Since they broke their truce with me I have killed every white man I could find. What makes you think that you will ever again see the sun go down over your own campfire?"

Jefford's face showed no fear as he answered calmly, "Because between brave men there is always honor."

Cochise raised his head proudly. His black eyes flashed. "Enju," he said. "We will talk."

Then he gave orders to his braves. He told the squaws to prepare a feast. They roasted deer and antelope and made cakes of mescal covered with flour made from the beans of the mesquite. They prepared sweet meal from ground hackberries, and brought great drafts of tiswin to drink.

When the feasting was over, Cochise led the way to his wickiup. He sat down on a blanket and motioned Jeffords to a place opposite him.

Cochise looked his guest in the eye, measuring him. He knew that he was brave. But was he wise? This, Cochise told himself, he would soon discover. He found himself strangely curious about this white man. Who was he? Whence did he come?

On the ground inside the wickiup lay the large leather pouch which had been taken from the dead body of the latest of the mail carriers whom Cochise's braves had ambushed and killed. Cochise noticed that Jeffords was looking at it. He chuckled.

"Yes," he said, as though Jeffords had queried him. "My braves took that from the body of a White Eye who was carrying it before they killed him."

"And what did you do with what was in the pouch?" Jeffords asked.

Cochise made a motion with his hands, describing how the

contents had been allowed to be blown away by the wind that swept the Stronghold. "Those things in the pouch had no value for us," he said. "We did not know what they were except that they were some kind of medicine of the White Eyes."

"They were letters," Jeffords explained. "The little marks on paper are to the white man what smoke signals are to the Apaches. These letters, which white men call 'mail,' bring messages from people far away to their friends here. The men whom your braves have killed are poor. They make their living carrying these messages—these signals—back and forth. They make no trouble. They do not want trouble. They are like the air which carries the smoke signals of the Apaches. Yet these men have been killed again and again by the braves of the Chiricahuas. I have come to ask you to allow these messengers to travel safely with their messages."

"Why should I permit them to do this?" Cochise's black eyes flashed. "These signals they carry bring war to the Apaches."

"That is not so," Jeffords explained. His tone was so reasonable and sincere that Cochise believed him. "Military signals are not carried in letters. They are carried by special messengers. I was once such a messenger for my government."

"You tell me this?" Cochise asked in surprise.

"I hide nothing," Jeffords replied. "I do not lie. I have come to talk to you, man to man. When the white men were at war with one another, I carried messages for the military. Now that war is over. But while it was going on I worked for my government. When there is a war every man must take one side or the other. But these letters which are carried in leather pouches by my men are not messages of war. They bring news of their families to men who are far from home."

"That is all that they say?" Cochise demanded. "There is nothing in these messages against the Indians?"

"That is right," Jeffords answered.

"I have heard of this war between the White Eyes," said Cochise. "I have never understood why the white men should kill each other. I thought that was only what they did to Indians," he said bitterly.

"This war was between the North and South of my country," Jeffords explained. "Men of the South wished to break away and form their own nation, but the North thought that we should all stay together—so we fought. There were other reasons, too," he continued. "Men of the South bought and sold other men—men with black skins. The people of the North believed that it was wrong for men—any men—white, black or red—to own another human being."

"And which side did you fight on?" asked Cochise. Then a smile illumined his face. "No need to answer that," he said. "You fought against those who would own other men. But now white men whether from the North or South unite in fighting the Indian."

He suddenly grew tense. His kindly manner changed.

"Why should I do what you ask?" he demanded hoarsely. "Why should I help the white man? What do I care if these messages—even though they be messages of peace—pass among you?" Then his voice became more human. "For many harvests," he went on, "I was the friend of the White Eyes. I protected them from bad Indians. How did they repay me? By treachery. For the lives of the white men I saved I was paid in death. White men are truce killers. It is not only the Chiricahuas who have been so treated. Everywhere the treachery of the White Eyes writes itself in death. That has always been so—from the earliest times."

Story after story Cochise then related of the Americans' betrayal of the Indians. He began with the old tale of Juan José, whose people were slaughtered by the trader Johnson. He told of his own betrayal by Lieutenant Bascom—the boy-soldier. When he spoke of that time his voice grew deep and guttural—his eyes flashed fire. He went on to tell of the wanton slaying of Mangas Coloradas, of Paramuca and many more.

"Time and again white men have gathered Indians together, promising to make peace," Cochise said. "And then they have shot or poisoned them. And you ask me to spare such people!"

Cochise stopped speaking. A deep silence fell between the two men. At last Jeffords spoke. "What you say is true, I know," he said. "You are right—and it is just that you should hate the white men who have injured your people. But the men I am asking you to spare have caused you no harm—nor do they wish you any harm."

"There are Indians who caused your people no harm," Cochise answered. "Yet they are hunted like wild animals and killed. Do the white men try to find out which Indians are bad and which are good?"

"No," Jeffords replied.

"Then what you ask is that I be better than the white men?" said Cochise.

"I ask you to be greater than they," Jeffords answered.

"You ask strange things of me," Cochise replied, gazing at his guest in wonder.

"There is no fork in my tongue," Jeffords answered. "I have come to see you—not knowing whether you would permit me to return alive to my people. If my time has come to its end tonight in the Stronghold of Cochise, the mighty chief of the Chiricahuas, I say 'so be it.' "

Cochise rose and, followed by Jeffords, walked to the edge of the cliff. While they talked the night had passed. Dawn was flushing the sky. The ridges of the distant mountains stood out sharp and clear in the cool air.

Cochise breathed deeply. Sweeping his arm out toward the

valleys and mountains, he said, "This is the country of the Men of the Rising Sun, whom you call Chiricahua Apaches. This is our home. It has always been our home. Long ago there were none here but Indians. Then there was plenty of food. Our people could all find enough to eat. First there came to our lands men with steel—the Spanish, you call them. They tried to take our land from us. We defeated them in battle. Then came the Mexicans"—the chief almost spat out that word. "Them, too, we defeated. But now the Americans have come—worse, far worse than either Spaniards or Mexicans—the truce killers. None are more arrogant than they. They make laws and say those laws are right and must be obeyed—Indians as well as Americans and Mexicans must obey them. Why do they do this?"

"I have asked myself that question many times," Jeffords said.

In the morning light Cochise studied the face of this strange white man. "I have seen you before," he said. "I think we have faced each other in battle at some time."

"That is true," Jeffords replied. "I fought in the great battle of Apache Pass."

"The day they shot at us with fire wagons," Cochise said, and his voice was bitter. "It is your red beard that I remember. We would have driven all of you White Eyes from the pass had it not been for those fire wagons."

"I had charge of those guns," Jeffords said, bravely. "I told the white soldiers where to place them."

There was profound respect in the eyes of the chief as he looked at Jeffords. "You are a brave man, Tagliato (Redbeard)," he said. "A very brave man."

Cochise's voice was deep. All hate and resentment was gone from it. Instead it held a note of sadness—sadness and infinite loneliness.

"Tagliato," the chief said, "we are friends."

"Yes," Jeffords answered. His voice, too, was heavy with emotion.

"I will do as you ask about those men of yours who carry the leather bags. They will never more be harmed by my braves. Do you believe me, Tagliato?"

"Yes," Jeffords replied. "We will never lie to each other. But our friendship will be a strange thing," he went on, after a moment of silence. "We will meet much opposition. Neither your people nor mine will understand us."

"You are not like other white men," Cochise said. "We will speak many times with each other, and never will we speak with a forked tongue. And no matter what our people do it will not affect what is between you and me. Another thing, your life will be safe among my people forever."

"I wish I could promise you the same," Jeffords replied softly. "But someday, perhaps, you, too, may walk among my people in safety."

"Let us rest," said Cochise. "The night is over and Holos is starting his trip across the sky."

Cochise assigned Jeffords a wickiup, a short distance away from his own, and watched his new friend throw himself upon a pallet and stayed beside him until he slept. A strange sense of peace enveloped the Apache chief. "Friendship is a great and good thing," he told himself. He had not felt like this since he and Naretena had held their last talk.

This truce between himself and Captain Jeffords in no wise affected the Chiricahua chief's war against the white men. This was between them alone, although it extended to include all of Jefford's mail carriers. The attacks on them ceased as if by magic. But Cochise's depredations against the whites in general went on as forcibly as ever.

On many different occasions the red-bearded white man went

to see Cochise at one or another of his rancherias. The admiration that these two had for one another grew with time. Indeed, it became something deeper than admiration, for they came to love each other as brothers.

Jeffords told the chief about his own early life. When he spoke of his days as captain of a steamboat which plied up and down the Mississippi River, and described that great river to Cochise, the chief said, "If any man but you told me of a river as large as you say this one is, Tagliato, I would think he was lying." For the conception of so much running water was beyond the ken of an Indian whose whole life had been spent in the barren wastes of the Southwest, where so little water flows that every drop is precious.

During one of their talks Cochise confessed that he was often haunted by the ghost of the Mexican he had tortured. Remorse, like pity, was an emotion which was believed to be unknown to the Apache. And when Cochise told his great friend that never in his whole life had he derived pleasure from torturing his helpless victims or in mutilating their dead bodies, Jeffords learned anew how different was this "savage" from most of his kind.

One time when Jeffords was visiting Cochise in the eastern Stronghold a furious storm arose. All during the night the wind sighed through the trees and whistled around the brush-covered wickiups of the Men of the Rising Sun. The shamans chanted and sang to ward off the evil influences of the wind, which, they believed, were the voices of the restless souls in the spirit land.

At last the rain came, heralded by a great streak of lightning. "My brother used to say that lightning is an arrow of the Thunder People," Cochise remarked.

Such a sentiment coming from the lips of the insensitive Juan, who seemed to have no interest in anything but killing men and animals, surprised Jeffords.

"Your brother?" he asked. "You mean Juan said that?"

"Not Juan," Cochise replied sadly. "My younger brother, whom I loved as I have loved no living person but you, Tagliato. It was he whom that treacherous boy-soldier hanged years ago." He paused and brooded for several moments. "Since his death I have made the white men pay for their treachery a hundred times over," he continued fiercely, through clenched teeth.

What a price had been paid, Jeffords thought to himself, what a terrible price because of one stupid and arrogant young shave-tail.

This talk had taken place some years after the first meeting between these two. A few months afterward, Jeffords was approached by Captain Farnsworth who wanted to engage him as a scout for the military, to lead soldiers against the Apaches. With great reluctance, Jeffords agreed, because he believed in all sincerity that there was no solution to the "Indian Problem" short of putting the tribes on reservations as quickly as possible. His heart was sick over all this ceaseless, useless warfare and bloodshed. His many attempts to persuade Cochise to surrender to the white men had failed over and over again. This new work, he realized, might lead him into open battle against his friend Cochise. He determined to go once more to see Cochise—to explain why he was undertaking this new work. While there, he would make one last effort to persuade him to put an end to this dreadful slaughter.

When Jeffords reached the east Stronghold, where Cochise and his band were encamped, he found it unnecessary to tell Cochise of his new assignment. As always, he was amazed to learn that even this action had reached the ears of the chief. For Cochise's scouts were ever on the alert to discover any new mischief on the part of their white enemies.

Cochise, Jeffords found, bore him no resentment. They discussed his scouting for the Americans simply and intelligently

—as two equals—not as a "red savage" and a white man of a "superior race."

"My people will lose in time, Tagliato," Cochise said. "The weak always lose in the end. We are not strong now, as we once were strong. Soon we will die—some slowly by starving on reservations, others in war. Now it is afternoon for the Apaches. Soon it will be night. Do not grieve that you are taking the warpath against me, Tagliato. We are more than our people—you and I. And now we shall be brothers."

"We are brothers, Cochise," Jeffords said.

"We shall become blood brothers," Cochise replied. "We will have a ceremony. We will mix our blood, and forever and ever what happens to one of us will be known and felt by the other."

Jeffords was amazed that Cochise should suggest this thing at such a time. He was humble before the very real greatness of this man, whom most white men called a "savage."

And so, Nochalo, greatest of the shamans, now that Nan-ta-do-tash was dead, made the preparations. There was no singing, no dancing, no beating of the tom-toms for this most sacred of all Apache ceremonies.

As had been done years before, when Cochise and Mangas Coloradas had been made blood brothers, the shaman made a cut in the arm of each man and allowed their blood to flow into a cup. Then he held their two arms together, so that one incision covered the other. And each man—the white and the red—drank their commingled blood.

"Shee-kizzen," Cochise said to Jeffords.

"My brother," Jeffords answered. They looked long and deeply into one another's eyes. Then Jeffords mounted his horse and rode away from the Stronghold.

Chapter 14

The Great Peace

THE WAR OF EXTERMINATION AGAINST THE APACHES WENT
on and on. By the year 1870, President Grant, discouraged over
the so-called "Indian Problem" in the Southwest, had inaug-
urated his famous Peace Policy. This met with some success,
and many of the tribes were settled on reservations.

One of the President's representatives, an idealistic Quaker,
named Colyer, attempted to fulfill Grant's orders to "locate the
nomadic tribes on suitable territories," but met with little luck,
being blocked on the one hand by American settlers, who
screamed for total extermination, and on the other by the Indians
themselves—for the Pinal Treaty, or, as it was also called, the

153

Pinole Treaty, was still too fresh in their minds to allow them to put any faith in the promises of the white man.

Colyer set apart the valley of the Tulerosa as a reservation for the Indians still on the warpath, but they did not like the location and only a few went there. The rest joined the Chiricahuas, and Colyer was recalled.

Cochise, persuaded by Jeffords, did go to the Canada Alamosa for a peace talk with General Granger, who was in charge. Granger offered the Chiricahua chief the Tulerosa as a reservation for his people.

"That is far away," Cochise replied, "and filled with flies that eat out the eyes of horses. Bad spirits live there. I have drunk of these waters and I do not want to leave this place."

So General Granger faithfully promised Cochise that his tribe could remain at Canada Alamosa for all time, and Cochise moved his tribe there. But within a few months they were ordered to move to the hated Tulerosa. At once the Chiricahuas took the warpath, and raiding and killing was resumed. The white man's broken promise again reaped its inevitable punishment.

Early in 1871, General George Crook came to Arizona from his successful campaigns against the Sioux in the North. Crook organized scouts from the Apaches themselves to lead his troops against their warring tribesmen. So the Chiricahuas resorted to their old tactics, making a number of simultaneous attacks over widely separated regions, and spreading terror over the whole territory.

Crook, known as the "Gray Fox" to the Indians, was called the "Terrible and Just" by the white men. Terrible he was, it was true—ruthless and unending were his attacks upon the Apaches. No doubt he was called "just" because he tried to reason with the Indians, pointing out to them that they would be much better off on reservations, and telling them that if they refused to go there, they would be hunted down until the last one was killed! "Just," indeed!

In one of his many talks with Cochise, Jeffords said that the only escape from utter extermination for the Chiricahuas was to take them to a reservation.

"Every year there are fewer of your tribesmen left," Jeffords said. "Bit by bit you are losing this war."

"What else can we do?" Cochise demanded. "What do our white brothers offer us? Do they try to make a just peace with us? No. There are no honest men with whom we can deal—there are only lies and broken promises. There is no reservation anywhere on our lands where Indians receive fair treatment—where they can live as men and braves. A reservation is only a large jail, and the Indians who go there are starved and mistreated."

"That is not the fault of the reservations, Cochise," Jeffords replied. "It is because of the men who govern them. If there were good Indian agents, reservations would be good, too."

"But there are no good agents, Tagliato," Cochise countered. "No, my brother, I would rather die with a bullet in my chest than starve to death in a jail run by lying white men. All white men I have ever met speak with a forked tongue, my brother. All except you. Tell me, Tagliato," he asked seriously, "why do men lie?"

"I do not know," Jeffords answered.

"A man should never lie," Cochise said.

"No, he should not," Jeffords said. "But a great many do."

"No man needs to lie," the chief said philosophically. "If someone asks you something that you do not wish to answer, you can say 'I do not want to talk about that.' White men treat us as though we were rattlesnakes or coyotes."

Jeffords made no reply, for he knew that that was indeed the attitude of most white men toward the Apaches.

Especially was he disgusted when he heard of the so-called "Camp Grant Massacre," when the peaceful Arivaipa Apaches, whose chief was the good Eskiminzin, were attacked by a band of men who were indignant because of a raid that had occurred near the town of Tucson. These white men were incensed at what they considered the "coddling" of the Apaches by a few of the more humane Indian agents. When the military refused to punish the Arivaipas, who had taken no part whatsoever in this raid, they took things into their own hands.

Early one April morning, together with some Mexicans and Papagos, they departed in secrecy from Tucson, with a wagon-load of arms and ammunition. While the Arivaipa Apaches were still sleeping in their wickiups, these self-styled "avengers" entered their camp. And before they left, one hundred and eight Arivaipas—mostly women and children—were left dead, their skulls beaten with clubs—because clubs make less noise than bullets! Many of the small children who had not been killed were presented to their Mexican confederates by these noble "avengers."

President Grant in faraway Washington ordered the governor of Arizona to arrest the perpetrators of this crime. They were all tried before a federal judge and jury. But after half an hour's deliberation the jury declared the defendants "not guilty."

When word of this latest outrage reached the ears of Cochise, he said, "Death of Apaches by starvation on reservations is too slow for the White Eyes, maybe."

President Grant, incensed at the result of his order, sent General Oliver O. Howard, a distinguished veteran of the Civil War, with full powers to make peace with the Apaches. Howard was a very different type of soldier from any who had heretofore attempted to deal with the Indian Problem. Although he was fully as great a humanitarian as Colyer, he was much more practical. He had received specific orders from the President to seek out Cochise and make peace with him if possible.

General Howard was well past middle age when he undertook this difficult assignment. His black beard was streaked with gray. He had lost his right arm in a battle of the Civil War, and wore the empty sleeve of his blue soldier's coat pinned up nearly to the shoulder.

He was a practicing Christian who really obeyed the principles of the Sermon on the Mount.

Some of the reports which reached Cochise said that this man was a different kind of white man—that as he went about among the various Indian tribes he was really working for their good. Perhaps—who knew?—this man might prove to be like his blood brother Tagliato. Cochise and his tribesmen might get justice at the hands of such a one.

Cochise was further impressed when he learned that General Howard had arranged to have the Arivaipa children—who had been given to the Mexicans at the time of the Camp Grant Massacre—returned to their own people. He wished he could discuss this man with his blood brother, Cochise thought. For, more and more, the Chiricahua chief was coming to share Jeffords' belief that the only hope for the salvation of the Chiricahuas was to make peace somehow with the white invaders. But Cochise would make no move toward meeting the general. He and his band remained as elusive as ever, and all of General Howard's attempts to get in touch with Cochise were futile.

The general had been told that there was only one white man in the whole territory who was friendly with the Apache chieftain. That man was Tom Jeffords.

One time, in a garrison in New Mexico, a tall, spare man with red hair and long red whiskers was pointed out to him as

"Tom Jeffords." Giving his own name, General Howard asked, "Is this Mr. Jeffords?"

"Yes, sir, that is my name," was the answer.

"Can you take me to the camp of the Indian, Cochise?" Howard asked.

Jeffords regarded the old soldier steadily for several minutes. Apparently he liked what he saw, for he said, "Will you go there with me, General, without soldiers?"

"Yes," General Howard replied, "if necessary."

"Then I will take you to him," Jeffords responded.

Howard was as impressed with the bravery and candor he read in Jeffords' face as the latter had been with him. So Jeffords arranged to have Chie, the son of Mangas Coloradas, go with them as a "guide and friendly witness."

Then began the long, tiring journey to the Stronghold of the great chief of the Chiricahuas. Besides Chie, Jeffords suggested taking Ponce, the son of a great friend of Cochise, whose father, too, had been killed by the white men.

Besides Howard, Jeffords, Chie and Ponce, the party included the general's aide Captain Sladen, an interpreter, two packers and a man who acted as both cook and driver of a four-wheeled "ambulance," as wagons were called in those days.

They followed one trail after another, day after day. Many times, along the way, Chie gathered grass and stalks of mesquite and built little fires that shot up quickly, making a cloud of black smoke.

Howard asked why he was doing that, and Ponce answered, "Pax, humo pax," which Jeffords translated as "Peace—peace smoke."

One time Chie began to bark like a coyote, and was answered by a similar bark that seemed to come from the hill. He ran up the steep slope of the hill and was met by another Apache— a scout sent by Cochise.

The scout told General Howard that he would have to reduce the size of his party if he wished to see the chief. So Howard obligingly dismissed everybody but Jeffords, the two Indians, Captain Sladen and himself.

On and on they traveled, camping at night beside the sparse water holes in that vast and rocky territory. At last, one morning when Howard had become almost convinced that this journey was fruitless, the Apaches began to make preparations to receive their chief. First there came in advance, riding full speed down the ravine, a single horseman, short and thickset, his face made even uglier by the black and vermilion paint upon it. He dismounted and embraced Jeffords.

"Is this the man?" Howard asked.

"No," Jeffords told him. "This is Juan—his brother."

Juan was soon followed by a fine-looking Indian—a younger man and two women, who were, so Jeffords told the general, Cochise, his younger son, his sister and the youngest of his three wives.

Cochise dismounted and saluted Jeffords affectionately. His tall, sinewy body looked strong in spite of his years. His face, like that of his brother was colored with vermilion. There were many silver threads in his long black hair.

The Chiricahua chieftain grasped General Howard's hand and said pleasantly, "Buenas dias, señor." Then he turned to Jeffords and said something to him in Apache. "He wants to know the purpose of your visit," Jeffords explained.

"The President of the United States has sent me to make peace between you and the white people," Howard answered.

"Nobody wants peace more than I do," Cochise said.

"Then," said the general, "as I have full power, we can make peace."

Cochise said that since coming from Canada Alamosa he had done no harm to anyone. "But I am poor," he went on. "It has been necessary to send out some of my young braves to obtain food and horses for our people." Then Cochise began to relate the long list of his grievances against the white men.

"I know of these things," General Howard said, when the chief paused. "But now there are two parties in the United States. One is hostile to the Indian, it is true, but the other party is friendly and it is they who are in power now. General Grant—the President of the United States, is at their head."

Howard told Cochise his plan for making them a reservation on the Rio Grande, where other Apaches, besides themselves, could live in peace.

"I have been there," Cochise answered, "and I like the country. Rather than not have peace I will go there and take as many of my people as I can. But I am afraid that that would break up my tribe. Why not give us Apache Pass? Give me that and I will protect all roads and see that no one's property is taken by Indians." As he said that, his dark eyes flashed and he lifted his head proudly.

"Perhaps we could do that," the general answered. "But it seems to me it would be better for the Chiricahuas to go to Alamosa. That is a good place. There is much water there. It would furnish your people with fine grazing land for your cattle. Much mescal grows there, too, and, as you know, there is good hunting in the mountains."

Cochise made no reply to those arguments. "How long will you stay here, General?" he asked. "Will you wait for my chiefs to come in so that I can consult with them?"

It never seemed to occur to the Chiricahua chief that he held the very lives of these white men in his hands.

"I came from Washington to make peace with you and your people," the general answered. "I will stay as long as is necessary to do this."

General Howard was surprised that Cochise found it necessary to consult the members of his tribe. Like most Americans, who knew little of their ways, he was under the misapprehension that an Apache chief was all-powerful with his tribesmen, not knowing what independent folk the Apaches were, nor that a man remained chief only so long as his edicts reflected the wishes of the tribe as a whole.

"It will take about ten days for my chiefs to get here," Cochise said. Then he ordered his scouts to go off in search of his chiefs.

Seated upon a blanket, with Jeffords and Howard near by, Cochise made a long speech, telling again of the wrongs his people had suffered at the hands of the white men. As he spoke, his whole manner changed. The pleasant expression left his face— his eyes flashed. The tones of his voice grew harsh and fierce.

"We were once a large people covering these mountains," Cochise said. "We lived well. When the Americans first came, we welcomed them as brothers. But how did they treat us? Their weapons scared away the deer and antelope upon which we lived. They took our water holes. One day, under a flag of truce, a white man seized me and some of my people and murdered all of them, one my brother." Tears filled the eyes of the chief as he spoke those words. Never in all the long years had Cochise ceased to mourn the loss of Naretena.

"Now," Cochise went on, "both Americans and Mexicans kill an Apache on sight. The Americans have been as treacherous as any Mexican who ever lived. But I have fought back. For every one of my people slain by Americans, ten of them have been killed. But I know how many are the Americans in this country—they are almost as numerous as the stars in the heavens, while every day Apaches grow less. Why must you shut us up on a reservation?" he asked suddenly. "We will make peace, and we will keep it faithfully. But let us go around free as Americans do."

"This country does not belong just to the Indians," Howard replied, in a quiet, reasonable voice. "All of us have an interest in it. In order to keep the peace we must fix boundaries. Suppose that some rough American prospectors should kill some of your band—or suppose some of your wild young braves should take the life of an American citizen. Then this peace we both want so much would be hopelessly broken."

Cochise considered the general's words for several minutes. Then he said harshly, "You Americans began this fight."

"That is true," replied the wise old general. "A large number of your friends among us believe that. But they want this senseless war to end."

Cochise regarded the general in whose face honesty and faith shone like a clear light. Then he smiled. "I am glad you came," he said. "But will not your soldiers fire on my braves if they see them coming here?"

Howard said he would send Captain Sladen to Fort Bowie with orders to allow all the Apaches to come in unharmed, and that he would notify the other army posts to do likewise.

"The American soldiers will not obey Captain Sladen," Cochise answered. "But they will obey you. I want you to go— and Captain Sladen and Tagliato can stay here while you are away."

So, taking Chie with him, the tired old man made his weary way over the Dragoon Mountains, then across the plains and deserts to the Chiricahua Mountains to Apache Pass where Fort Bowie was located. Cochise and several of the Indians accompanied the general for several miles. Stopping on some high ground that afforded a panoramic view of the magnificent surrounding hills and valleys, Cochise raised his eyes and looked all about him. "Shi-cowah!" (My home!) he exclaimed proudly.

For several days after his return, General Howard lived with the Chiricahuas. The camping ground to which Cochise led them was north of the entrance to his Stronghold. Six miles up the hill was a rock that sprang up three hundred feet from the plain, with the San Pedro River at its foot. Here Cochise requested Jeffords and Captain Sladen to place a white flag. When this was done the women and children of the tribe danced and clapped their hands, saying a long word in their own tongue, which Jeffords translated as meaning, "The flag of peace I love."

The first evening after Howard's return, the Chiricahuas gave a dance in his honor. Some of the women invited the general to join the dance, which he did. One squaw held his left hand and another took hold of his empty right sleeve. Howard laughed and joked with the people, endearing himself to all of them.

The Chiricahuas noticed the little black Bible which the general always carried. They believed it must be some powerful "medicine" of the white man's because of the reverent expression which illumined the old man's face whenever he looked into it.

At night, some of the smallest children of the camp crowded around the kind old general as he stretched out on the ground in his wickiup, laying their little heads on his blanket. "This does not mean war," the general said to Jeffords.

One after another, the bands of warriors returned to the Stronghold. Some of the newcomers were rough and troublesome, and Howard soon saw that he must abandon his plan of using the Alamosa for the Chiricahua reservation.

When they had all come in, a strange meeting took place. The muffled sound of the voices of many women, who were apparently imitating the low moaning of the wind, reached the ears of the three white men, who were anxiously waiting. The singing, if it could be called that, rose higher and higher in ever increasing volume.

"What are they doing?" Howard asked Jeffords.

"They are holding a sort of prayer meeting," Jeffords replied. "They are consulting their spirits, asking for guidance."

"Let us pray that their spirits will be on our side," General Howard spoke fervently. "I think we should pray to our 'spirit,' too."

He knelt on the ground and closed his eyes. And Tom Jeffords, who had not knelt in prayer since he was a child in his home in Chautauqua, in the state of New York, got down beside the general, and together they asked *their* God that this meeting bring peace.

Shortly thereafter a tall, muscular Apache ran up to their wickiup and invited them to join the Chiricahuas on the plateau. The three white men sat among the squaws outside the circle of braves. Then the authoritative voice of Cochise rang out. Howard did not understand the words, although he guessed that the chief was laying the peace plan before his braves.

Those were solemn, anxious moments for the good general. But apparently both the God of the white men and the spirits of the Indians were in accord. Their answer was given by Cochise with these momentous words: "Hereafter the white man and the Indian are to drink of the same water, eat of the same bread and be at peace."

On the following day they all set out to meet with army officers from Camp Bowie at Dragoon Springs. Cochise and all his braves were dressed in their war garments, their faces bright with paint.

When they arrived at Dragoon Springs, Cochise placed his men with such skill that everyone of them could, in two minutes' time, have gotten safely under the cover of a ravine—and in three minutes more have escaped behind a protecting hill. "No white general could have placed his men more strategically," Howard commented admiringly to Sladen.

Cochise turned to Jeffords, "I know your party and I trust you, but these men from Fort Bowie I do not know. How long have you known them?"

"I never saw them before," Jeffords answered.

The meeting with Major Sumner and several officers and a few civilians was entered into at once. It lasted four hours. And at the end, however, peace was assured. The metes and bounds of the reservation were laid out in the territory Cochise desired, with the agency located at Sulphur Springs.

Cochise made one stipulation—and about that he was adamant. He insisted that his blood brother, Tom Jeffords, be made agent for the Chiricahuas.

At first Jeffords stoutly refused. He knew the problems an Indian agent must face; he knew, too, how hard it would be to get supplies to the Apaches, with almost everyone in the whole territory of Arizona blocking him all along the way. When he refused, Cochise said firmly, "Then there will be no peace," and rose to leave, followed by his braves.

General Howard pleaded with Jeffords, and at last he complied. But he made certain conditions which Howard was obliged to grant. He must be absolute boss, answerable only to the Department of the Interior at Washington, with no interference by either the military or the citizenry of the territory.

Rather than lose this peace so hardly won, Howard agreed to everything Jeffords stipulated.

And so the Great Peace was made between the white men and the red.

Back at the Stronghold in the Dragoons, General Howard placed a large stone upon a mesa. "Peace between our people shall continue as long as this stone shall last," the great general said humbly—"Please God."

Chapter 15

To the Happy Hunting Grounds

GENERAL HOWARD LAID OUT THE RESERVATION FOR THE Chiricahuas in that portion of what is now known as Cochise County in southeastern Arizona lying east of the Dragoon Mountains. Here, with Tom Jeffords, blood brother of Cochise as agent, the tribe settled down to live as wards of the United States Government.

The powereful old chief of the Chiricahuas was always at Jeffords' right hand, seeing that every order he issued was scrupulously obeyed. Many times disgruntled warriors from other tribes tried to persuade Cochise and his braves to join them in attacks upon the white men, but he remained absolutely faithful to his word.

The visitors to the Chiricahua Reservation were not only the malcontents from other tribes, however. The governor of Arizona, A. P. K. Safford, journeyed to the east Stronghold to see how Jeffords was getting on as agent for the most "bloodthirsty" savages on the North American continent, as most people in those days considered the Chiricahuas.

Cochise greeted the governor cordially, although he slyly remarked to Jeffords that "now I am something to be seen, like an animal in a cage."

"Yes," Jeffords agreed, "a tamed lion." And the two friends laughed together.

The governor was greatly impressed, both with the character of the chief and the respect given Jeffords by Cochise and all his followers. This was because Agent Jeffords strictly enforced his rule of refusing to allow either soldiers or civilians to come upon the reservation without his permission.

He ordered—and Cochise obeyed this order—that all stolen horses and other ill-gotten goods in the possession of the Chiricahuas at the time peace was declared be returned to their owners.

Jeffords treated those formerly warlike Apaches as a friend as well as a guardian. He did his best to safeguard their interests in every way and to see that they received justice. He refused to go through all the red tape and other unnecessary rigmarole practiced on other Indian reservations. And he made his reports directly to the Department of the Interior at Washington, D. C.

Jeffords' attitude was considered very highhanded by the local authorities, and he often found it difficult to get the supplies allotted by government order to the Chiricahuas. For the so-called "Tucson Ring," that group of money-hungry men who hoped that Jeffords would make a failure of the Chiricahua Reservation, stood in his way.

"They don't want us to succeed, Cochise," Jeffords told the chief. "They can't believe that you really mean to stop your depredations."

"We will succeed, my brother," Cochise reassured him, again and again.

And now that peace was fully established and no tribes in Arizona were on the warpath, it was safe for the first time since white men had come into the territory for one of them to travel anywhere north of the Mexican border.

Sometimes during the two years that Cochise lived in peace and quiet on the reservation, thefts were committed and cases of whisky peddling went on with their inevitable accompaniment of murder—times when the restless young braves from the White Mountain Reservation tried to persuade the Chiricahuas to rise up and leave their reservation. Working together, however, Cochise and Jeffords took care of all these things as they occurred. They ferreted out the criminals, hunted down the whisky peddlers and drove the malcontents from other tribes away.

And because there was no appeal beyond their judgment—and because no hungry politician could make it came to pass that his charges were swindled or robbed of their rations—Jeffords, with the help of Cochise, was able to enforce their rules and keep the peace.

For the past several years Cochise had been suffering from a painful illness. Often he was in such agony that he was unable to eat. One day in 1874, at the time of year the Apaches called "Many Leaves" (June), Cochise was too sick to leave his blanket. For four days he lay ill, while outside his wickiup the medicine man moaned and wailed and shook his gourd and made his "medicine" to drive away the evil spirits who he believed were at work trying to kill his chief.

But the medicine man's efforts were to no avail. When Tesalbestinay realized that her husband was dying, she sent his eldest son Tahzay posthaste to the agency building to summon Jeffords.

Jeffords, knowing how ill Cochise was, hurried across the miles with all possible speed.

"Look after my people when I am no longer here, Shee kizzen," Cochise said.

"That is very well," Jeffords replied, "but I am only one and they are many. They won't do what I want them to unless they themselves want it, too."

So Cochise called in the headmen of his tribe, and in their presence he selected his eldest son Tahzay to be his successor, winning from them a promise that they would always do what Jeffords wished, and forever walk the "white man's road" in peace.

Then Jeffords, watching at the bedside of the great chief, tried to persuade him to take some medicine to relieve his pain. But Cochise was too much an Indian to have any faith in the bottled medicine of the white man.

As a proof of his great affection for Jeffords, Cochise presented him with his favorite possession—a double-barreled shotgun which he prized, as he said, as much as he did an arm or a leg.

Jeffords was needed at the agency to issue rations to the Apaches in his care. As he rose to go, Cochise said, "Do you think you will see me alive again?"

"No, I do not think I will," Jeffords replied, for between these two there had always been absolute honesty. "I think by this time tomorrow night you will be dead."

Then Cochise said, "I think so, too." He was silent for a moment, then spoke in a low, vibrant voice. "Do you think we will ever meet again, Shee-kizzen?"

Jeffords was taken aback. "I don't know," he said. "What do you think?"

"I have been thinking about it a good deal while I have been sick, and I believe we will. Good friends will meet again—up there."

"Where?" Jeffords asked.

"That I do not know. Somewhere up yonder, I think," Cochise answered, pointing to the sky.

And so the two friends parted for the last time, pondering the question that has puzzled men of every race in every land since time began.

Jeffords rode away, leaving Tesalbestinay with Cochise. When she believed the end was near she called his two sons Tahzay and Nachise in to see their father.

Cochise looked at them for a long time.

"You have been good sons to me," he said. "Before I made the great peace with Nantan Howard, we were often on the warpath together. You were always brave. Now I am going to leave you for all time. I do not know where I am going, but sometime again we will meet, I think. Maybe I will see Nachi, my father, and Alope, my mother, and my good brother Naretena and the great Mangas Coloradas, too. I do not know, but I believe I will.

"When I am gone Tahzay will be chief of all the Men of the Rising Sun. And Tahzay will keep the peace I have made with the Americans—and Nachise will help him."

The dying chief waited for an answer.

"Enju," they said together. "It shall be done."

Cochise closed his eyes as a great wave of pain swept through him. In a moment he spoke again.

"One thing more I want. Holos has not yet climbed over the mountain in the east. I want to see the sun once more, but I have not long to wait."

Tahzay and Nachise called four strong young braves who tenderly placed the dying chief on a litter. Up the rough trail they carried him to the ridge above the Stronghold. Silently the people of his tribe followed. As the sun showed its face over the mountain, the soul of the great Cochise departed to the happy hunting grounds.

All day and all night the wailing and moaning of his people echoed through the mountains and valleys of the Stronghold. At daylight the following morning everyone was silent. The rule of not allowing women and children to go to the burials of of members of the Chiricahuas was relaxed in this case.

They dressed Cochise in his finest garments, decorated his face with war paint and put eagle feathers on his head. Then he was mounted on his favorite horse with one of his braves holding his body in place on either side. Followed by all the Chiricahuas, he was guided to a rough and lonely place midst the rocks of the Stronghold, where there was a deep cave in the cliff.

His horse was killed and dropped into the depths of the cave. His favorite dog was dealt with in the same manner. His bows and arrows, lances and other arms were thrown in, too.

As the body of Cochise was lowered into his sepulcher, high in the air above their heads an eagle screamed.

In order that no one would ever know where their chief was buried the braves of his tribe pretended that it was somewhere on the mesa at the entrace to the Stronghold. To give credence to this story, they rode their horses back and forth over this pretended grave as though they were obliterating all traces of its exact location in order that no one might ever be able to identify the spot. Apart from the members of his tribe, no one but Thomas Jeffords ever knew the truth, and although he outlived Cochise by forty years he never divulged the secret.

After the burial all of the members of the tribe except one returned to their wickiups. Tesalbestinay sat for hours before the tomb of her lord, her head covered with a blanket, her grief too deep for tears.

Bibliography

Adams, Ward R., *History of Arizona*. Record Publishing Company, 1930.

Arnold, Elliott, *Blood Brother*. Duell Sloan and Pearce, 1947.

Arnold, Elliott, "Cochise—Greatest of Apaches." *Readers Digest*, April, 1951.

Baker, Sherman, "Blood Brother of the Apaches." *Desert Magazine*, November, 1942.

Bancroft, H. H., *History of Arizona and New Mexico*. The History Company, 1889.

Bartlett, John Russell, *Personal Narrative of Exploration and Incidents*. D. Appleton & Company, 1854.

Bechdolt, Frederick R., *When the West Was Young*. N. Y. Century Company, 1922.

Bleeker, Sonia, *Apache Indians*. William Morrow & Company, 1951.

Blount, Bertha, "Apache in the Southwest." *Southwestern Historical Quarterly*, 1919.

Bourke, John G., *Apache Campaign in Sierra Madre*. Charles Scribner's Sons, 1886.

Bourke, John G., *On the Border with Crook*. Charles Scribner's Sons, 1891.

Browne, J. Ross, "Tour Through Arizona." *Harper's New Magazine*, 1864.

Burgess, Opie Rundle, "Early Arizona History." (From unpublished manuscript).

Burroughs, Edgar Rice, *War Chief*. Grosset & Dunlap, 1927.

Clum, Woodworth, *Apache Agent, The Story of John P. Clum.* Houghton, Mifflin Company, 1936.

Comfort, William Levington, *Apache.* E. P. Dutton & Company, 1931.

Conkling, Roscoe P. and Margaret B., *Butterfield Overland Mail.* The Arthur H. Clark Company, 1947.

Connell, Charles T., "Apache Past and Present." *Tucson Citizen,* February to July, 1921.

Corle, Edwin, *Gila, The River of the Southwest.* Rinehart & Company, 1951.

Cremony, John C., "Apache Race, The." *Overland Magazine,* 1868.

Cremony, John C., *Life Among the Apaches.* A. Roman & Company, 1868.

Cremony, John C., "Some Savages." *Overland Magazine,* March, 1872.

Dobie, J. Frank, *Mustangs, The.* Little, Brown & Company, 1952.

Dunn, J. P. Jr., *Massacres of the Mountains.* Harper & Brothers, 1886.

Eastman, Edwin, Seven Years Among the Comanches and Apaches. (From unpublished Manuscript), 1874.

Farish, Thomas Edwin, *History of Arizona.* Filmer Brothers, 1941.

Federal Writers Project, *Arizona.* Hastings House, 1940.

Goddard, Pliny Earle, *Indians of the Southwest.* Museum of Natural History, N. Y. (Handbook Series), 1931.

Goodwin, Grenville, *Social Organization of the Western Apache.* University of Chicago Publications in Anthropology.

Goodwin, Grenville, *Southern Athapascan Clans.* The University of Chicago Press, 1942.

Hamilton, Patrick, *Resources of Arizona*. A. L. Bancroft Publishing Company, 1883.

Heald, Weldon F., "Cochise Stronghold." *Arizona Highways*, May, 1949.

Hodge, Frederick Webb, *Handbook of the American Indians*. Government Printing Office, Washington, D. C.

Howard, General O. O., *Famous Indian Chiefs I Have Known*. The Century Company, 1908.

Howard, General O. O., *My Life and Experiences Among Our Hostile Indians*. A. D. Worthington & Company, 1907.

Humfreville, J. Lee, *Twenty Years Among Our Hostile Indians*. Hunter Company, 1899.

Lockwood, Frank C., *Apache Indians*. The Macmillan Company, 1938.

Lockwood, Frank C., "Cochise, the Noble Warrior." *Arizona Highways*, 1939.

Lockwood, Frank C., *Pioneer Days in Arizona*. The Macmillan Company, 1932.

Lummis, Charles F., *Land of Poco Tiempo, The*. Charles Scribner's Sons, 1897.

Miller, Joseph, Editor, *The Arizona Story*. Hastings House, 1952.

Murdock, John R., "Arizona Characters in Silhouette." *Bulletin Arizona State Teachers College*.

Opler, Morris Edward, *An Apache Life-Way*. University of Chicago Press, 1941.

Opler, Morris Edward, *Chiricahua Apache Social Organization*. Social Anthropology of North American Tribes, 1937.

Opler, Morris Edward, "Dirty Boy—A Jicarilla Tale of Raid and Warfare." Memoirs of American Anthropological Association, 1938.

Opler, Morris Edward, *Myths and Tales of the Chiricahua Apaches*. American Folklore Society, Vol XXXVII, 1942.

Opler, Morris Edward and Harry Hoijer, *Raid and Warpath Language of the Chiricahua Apaches*. The American Anthropological Association, 1949.

Opler, Morris Edward, "Themes as Dynamic Forces in Culture." *The American Journal of Sociology*, 1946.

Reagon, Albert B., "Notes on the Indians of the Fort Apache Region." *The Anthropological Papers of the American Museum of Natural History, Vol. XXXI*.

Rockfellow, John A., "The Story of Cochise Stronghold." (Taken from pamphlet).

Russell, Frank, "An Apache Medicine Dance." *American Anthropologist*, 1898.

Safford, Govenor A.P.K., "Something About Cochise." *Arizona Citizen*, December, 1872.

Santee, Ross, *Apache Land*. Charles Scribner's Sons, 1947.

Spence, Lewis, *Myths and Legends of the North American Indians*. D. D. Nickerson Company, 1914.

Spring, John A., "Troublous Days in Arizona." (From an unpublished manuscript).

Schwatka, Frederick, "Among the Apaches." *Century Magazine*, 1887.

Tassin, A. G., "Among the Apaches." *Overland Magazine*, 1889.

Wellman, Paul, *Death in the Desert*. The Macmillan Company, 1935.

Wood, Charles Morgan, "Forbes Notes." (Taken from pamphlet).

Wylls, Rufus K., *Arizona, The History of a Frontier State*. Hobson & Herr, 1950.

Index

About the Author

ENID JOHNSON was born in Indi-
anapolis, Indiana, attended schools there,
in Fort Wayne and New York City. She
was particularly interested in singing,
and came to New York to study voice.
After trying various phases of show business, she realized that a musical career
was not for her. Next followed a variety
of jobs and while working for a civic
club she met Anne Merriman Peck who
asked her to collaborate on a travel book.
This started Miss Johnson as an author,
and soon she was writing books on her
own for children and teen-agers. Her
varied experiences come through in her
many books: career fiction, biographies,
adventure stories. Miss Johnson now
lives in Tucson, Arizona.